May, 1981

Dear Paul,

many thanks for the
warm friendship I felt
during my stay in N.Y.
I would like to return the
hospitality someday in Aussieland.

Jan.

P.S. Was good to learn that
we great minds think alike....!

AUSTRALIAN REPTILES IN COLOUR

FRONTISPIECE

Bynoe's Gecko (*Heteronotia binoei*), one of the most common and wide-spread of Australian reptiles. Rarely more than 4 inches long, it is a ground-dwelling lizard which is found in a wide range of environments, from the deserts of the interior to the coastal regions in nearly all areas except south-eastern Australia. The specimen illustrated is from the coast of the Northern Territory. [Photo Author]

AUSTRALIAN REPTILES IN COLOUR

HAROLD COGGER

REED

First published 1967
Reprinted 1971, 1975, 1978

A. H. & A. W. REED PTY LTD
53 Myoora Road, Terrey Hills, Sydney
65-67 Taranaki Street, Wellington
11 Southampton Row, London
also at
Auckland and Christchurch

National Library of Australia
Cataloguing in Publication data

Cogger, Harold G.
    Australian reptiles in colour/ [by] Harold Cogger.
    Terrey Hills, N.S.W.: Reed, 1967.
    Index.
    ISBN 0 589 50060 0

    1. Reptiles — Australia. I. Title.

    598.10994

Printed and bound by Kyodo Printing Co Ltd, Tokyo

INTRODUCTION

MORE THAN 400 species of reptiles are known from Australia and the purpose of this small book is to serve as an introduction to this rich and varied fauna. It is not intended as a guide to the identification of Australian reptiles, although it should enable the reader to recognise without difficulty the group, or family, to which any particular reptile belongs. Nor has any attempt been made to discuss the general characteristics of reptiles, as such information is readily available in a host of technical and popular books. Rather, the general biology and characteristics of each family occurring in Australia are briefly outlined, while some of the more common or interesting species and their habits are described. The plates have been carefully chosen to supplement the text, the species illustrated being for the most part common and widely distributed. However, the occasional rare or bizarre form is also illustrated where it is needed to show the range of variation occurring in any particular family.

Scientific names have been used in conjunction with common names throughout the book. The principal reason for this is the stability and universal recognition of scientific names. Common names, on the other hand, are lacking for many groups or species of Australian reptiles, while still others have several common names, in use in different parts of the country.

Unfortunately, scientific names are not always as stable as they should be, and this instability tends to be directly related to the need for research into the classification of any group of animals. For the reader who finds inconsistencies between the scientific names in this book and those used in other books on Australian reptiles, the explanation is that the relationships of various reptiles, as reflected in their scientific classification, is subject to different interpretations by different biologists.

The aim of systematics, as the science of classification is called, is twofold. It aims, first, at establishing a stable system of scientific names, and second, at showing the inter-relationships of animals. There is no doubt that an increasing volume of modern research will bring about drastic changes in the classification of Australian reptiles.

Only those changes which have been accepted by the majority of the world's herpetologists have been incorporated in this book. There is certainly much to be said for "official" lists of names established by national organisations, as has been done for birds and some other animal groups in most countries.

The Evolution, Origins and Relationships of Australian Reptiles

The rate of evolution of animal species is generally encouraged by geographic barriers to an animal's distribution, such as deserts or mountain ranges, for these tend to isolate populations of animals from one another and to permit them to evolve along independent lines.

Yet despite the fact that Australia lacks the diversity of climate, topography, and environment that is exhibited by most continental areas of similar size in other parts of the world, and that for many millions of years it has had a relatively stable geological history, it has managed to evolve a reptile fauna that, in numbers and variety, compares more than favourably with that of other parts of the world. It is largely their diversity and evolutionary history that make the reptile fauna of Australia such a rich and valuable subject for study.

Although the animals of today can often provide information about the more recent past, the origins of all but the more recent reptilian arrivals to this country are fairly obscure. It is generally assumed that the whole of our reptile fauna arrived in Australia via South-east Asia and the Indo-Australian Archipelago; indeed, our more recent reptilian migrants have clearly used this route to reach Australia. Even those groups such as the goannas, skinks, dragons, and elapid snakes, all of which have had a long evolutionary history in Australia, have clear links with their relatives in Africa, Asia, and Indo-Malaysia. However, in reptiles, as in other animals, there are certain groups whose origins and relationships are much more obscure, and which are therefore much more difficult to explain.

The Chelid or Side-necked Tortoises and their relatives, for example, are found only in Madagascar, Africa, Australia, New Guinea, and South America. Attempts have been made to explain this unusual distribution (which is duplicated in many groups of animals and plants) in two ways.

One theory is that such groups were once more widely distributed in both hemispheres, but their subsequent extinction in the northern hemisphere has resulted in the distribution we see today. Another theory is that of "drifting continents", which proposes that the major land masses in the southern hemisphere were originally closely linked to form one major continental mass very different in shape and position from what we see on the maps of today. Subsequently, this mass broke up and the continents that we know today "drifted" into their present positions. This theory has in recent years received considerable support from geologists measuring magnetism in the earth's crust, but whether it can be used to solve all the problems of animal distribution claimed by its proponents remains to be seen.

In more recent times climatic changes associated with the cycle of alternate accumulation and melting of ice in the polar regions during the Great Ice Ages of the Pleistocene Period (between 10,000 and 1,000,000 years ago) resulted in numerous changes in sea-level. These sea-level changes were accompanied by radical changes in climate in various parts of the world.

It has already been mentioned that Australia lacks the diversity of topography and environments of most other continents. For this reason, one of the greatest problems facing the animal geographer in Australia is to explain the richness of the reptile life of the arid and semi-arid interior of Australia.

Livistona palms found in Palm Valley in Central Australia are now found elsewhere only in the wet coastal forests of eastern Australia. In South Australia have been found the fossils of crocodiles which now live only 1,000 miles to the north. These are just two examples of many which show clearly that, in Pleistocene times, parts of what is now desert or semi-desert were much wetter, with permanent lakes, streams and forests.

The probable distribution of these wetter areas, and the climatic patterns which produced them have long been debated by biologists and geologists. It nevertheless seems clear from the diversity of our desert fauna and the geological stability of many of the desert sand-ridge areas of inland Australia, that our deserts have long been a highly significant part of the Australian scene.

At some time during the Pleistocene the wet forests of south-eastern and south-western Australia, and the animals they contained, became isolated from each other by the intrusion of a broad band of desert in the region of the Nullabor Plain. The animals and plants of the south-west continued to evolve in isolation, producing many of the distinctive animals which occur there today.

It has been mentioned already that climatic changes associated with the Great Ice Ages of the Pleistocene were accompanied by numerous changes in the earth's sea-level. On several occasions the sea-level around Australia dropped by more than 300 feet, an amount greater than the present depth of water between Australia and Tasmania to the south, and Australia and New Guinea to the north. This resulted in land connections between these areas, allowing an exchange of animals and plants. The most recent of these land connections is believed to have existed as little as 12,000–20,000 years ago, and it was probably at this time that Tasmania was colonised by most, if not all, of the reptiles found there today, for they are all essentially the same as species found in south-eastern Australia.

The picture in the north is more complex, for the reptiles of eastern Australia show clearly the result of several interchanges between New Guinea and Australia. The Colubrid snakes probably arrived in Australia in one of the earliest of these migrations, while strict rain-forest inhabitants, such as the Angle-headed Dragons, the Green Tree Python, and certain skinks, appear to have migrated to Australia via the most recent land bridge between the two countries. Although Australia received numerous forms from New Guinea at this time, still others went in the opposite direction. The Sand Goanna, the Taipan, and the Carpet Snake are examples of reptiles that appear to have colonised New Guinea from Australia.

Hence it can be seen that the study of Australia's reptiles and other groups of animals can help to shed light on the more recent history of the climate, geology and vegetation of our island continent.

CONSERVATION OF REPTILES

The conservation of reptiles has been receiving considerable attention in recent years. Only two groups of reptiles in Australia have yet proved of economic importance – the crocodiles, and the large marine turtles. The former are sought for their skins while the Green Turtle has from time to time been sought commercially for food. Crocodiles and marine turtles are protected in Western Australia, the Northern Territory and Queensland. The natural populations of these reptiles can be seriously depleted by uncontrolled hunting, so that this statutory protection by the States together with the prohibition on the export of turtle and crocodile products by the Commonwealth seem necessary if they are to survive. Varying degrees of statutory protection are now afforded other reptiles in most Australian States.

But for most reptiles, as with the majority of other animals, ultimate survival will depend not on legal protection but on survival of the environment in which they live. Australia is a large country with vast, untapped natural resources which must, eventually, be utilised. The destruction of the natural environment more often than not is an irreversible process, so that failure to preserve significant samples of each major environment or habitat for future generations is as morally wrong as it is economically short-sighted. We have the enormous advantage of seeing the present plight of countries whose "development" preceded ours, yet we seem unable to learn our lesson.

FIRST-AID TREATMENT OF SNAKE-BITE

In the chapter on elapid snakes, the nature and use of snake-bite sera, or antivenenes, are discussed at length. Antivenenes normally are administered only by a qualified medical practitioner, and a person bitten by a snake should reach a doctor, or better still a hospital, as quickly as possible. In the meantime, the layman should carry out first-aid procedures as soon as possible after the bite occurs.

Even today medical authorities throughout the world disagree among themselves as to what constitute the most effective first-aid procedures in the case of snake-bite. Although incision of the bitten area, the sucking of blood from the wound and the use of potassium permanganate were all once recommended, the consensus of medical opinion today is against such methods. Each of them can have decided benefits under certain circumstances (as when the bite is not on a limb) but they are generally best avoided. Fortunately, nearly all bites occur on a limb.

Probably the most effective and practical first-aid procedure for snake-bite is that laid down in a recent report by the Royal Society of Tropical Medicine and Hygiene, which, in slightly modified form, consists of:

1. Kill the snake and handle it only by the tail. Keep it.
2. Apply a tight ligature around a single-boned part of the limb (the thigh or upper arm) between the bite and the body. A handker- chief, piece of cloth, or ideally a length of flexible rubber tube can be used as a ligature. First tie it loosely around the limb then tighten it by passing a stick or similar object through the loop and twisting it. The ligature should be loosened for 30–60 seconds about every 20–30 minutes, and can be dispensed with after two hours. The sooner the ligature is applied after the bite the more effective it will be. Ideally it should be applied within 30–60 seconds.
3. As the commonest symptoms are fright and fear of death, convincing reassurance is vital at all times. Death from snake-bite is rare.
4. Keep the patient at rest.
5. Wash the bitten surface with clean water (or urine if water is not available) without rubbing.
6. Keep the bitten part still, as one would for a fracture, and if possible keep it in a hanging position.
7. Administer a pain-killer (such as aspirin) but **not** morphia.
8. Call a doctor or, better still, get the patient to a hospital as soon as possible (with the dead snake, whenever possible).

ACKNOWLEDGMENTS

Many friends and colleagues, through discussions at the Australian Museum and on field expeditions, have contributed to the contents of this book.

For their help, encouragement and criticism I am especially grateful to my wife, Heather, to Miss Patricia McDonald, and to Mrs Robyn Brewer. I am grateful also to Mr S. Breeden for contributing his excellent photographs.

H. G. COGGER

CONTENTS

CROCODILES

Family Crocodylidae

ONLY TWO SPECIES of crocodiles are found in Australia, both restricted to the coastal and near-coastal areas of the northern tropical parts of the continent. These are the Fresh-water Crocodile (*Crocodylus johnstoni*), a narrow-snouted, fish-eating species normally found in fresh-water streams and lagoons; and the Estuarine or Salt-water Crocodile (*Crocodylus porosus*) (Plate 1), a large sea-going species usually found only in coastal or estuarine waters. Although it sometimes travels far up into the fresh-water reaches of large rivers, it is found in closed bodies of fresh water only when stranded there by receding floodwaters. The Fresh-water Crocodile occurs only in northern Australia, whereas the Estuarine Crocodile is widely distributed from India through Malaysia and Indonesia to New Guinea and northern Australia.

All crocodiles are remarkably similar in basic structure. The body is heavy and muscular, and well armoured; the skin is thick and leathery and is strengthened on the back by a series of close-set bony plates (termed osteoderms) just below the surface of the skin. The underside of the crocodile is partly protected by a series of gastralia or so-called abdominal ribs, which are not attached to the main skeleton. Of all other living reptiles the Tuatara of New Zealand is the only one which also possesses gastralia.

The skull of a crocodile is strongly built and armed with numerous sharp teeth which make it a formidable predator. The teeth are used only for grasping the prey and not for chewing, for the food is swallowed whole or in large sections.

The limbs are relatively short and thick-set. The forelimb has five toes which have only a trace of webbing at their base, whereas the hind limb has only four toes which are extensively webbed. In swimming the forelimbs are folded back along the body to give minimum resistance to the flow of the body through water, while the webbed hind feet are used for balance and for "treading water". In the water the heavy muscular tail is the main source of propulsion.

The Estuarine Crocodile averages less than 15 feet in length and although specimens exceeding 30 feet have been doubtfully recorded, individuals over 20 feet are rarely found. When adult it feeds on virtually any vertebrate animals that it can catch – fishes, tortoises and turtles, lizards and snakes, birds and mammals. The latter, including man, are usually caught when they come to the water to drink or bathe. Once seized in the powerful jaws they are held under the water until they drown.

This ability to drown their prey while they themselves remain unaffected below the water's surface is common to all crocodiles and is due to several remarkable structural features. First, the nostrils are equipped with fleshy valves which close off the air passages when their owner is submerged. Second, so that the mouth can remain open under water (to hold the prey), there is a fold of tissue on the upper surface of the base of the tongue which meets a similar fold on the palate. These can completely seal off the mouth from the respiratory passages, preventing water from entering the lungs. As a further adaptation the bones on the roof of the mouth form a complete secondary palate, as in mammals, so that the passage from the nostrils enters the throat behind the level of the two folds of tissue.

The female Estuarine Crocodile lays her eggs during the northern wet season, usually in January or February but sometimes as early as November or as late as April. Using her hind feet she scrapes together a nest about 5 or 6 feet across and up to 2 feet deep, made of grass, litter, and mud, on a river bank out of reach of

Plate 1. A sub-adult specimen of the Estuarine Crocodile (*Crocodylus porosus*) photographed in a paperbark swamp on the eastern headland of Port Essington in the Northern Territory. The red objects on either side of the crocodile's head are ripe fruits of the Pandanus palm. [Photo Author]

high tides. Within this nest she subsequently lays up to about 70 white, brittle-shelled eggs, 2½–3 inches long, which she covers with mud and vegetation. The decaying vegetable matter in the nest provides heat to assist in incubation. During the earlier part of the incubation period the mother remains in the general vicinity of the nest, returning periodically to repair it if necessary, but as the time for hatching approaches her visits become more frequent. Under normal conditions the eggs hatch between two and three months after being laid and when they are ready to hatch the young can be heard faintly squeaking within the nest. It has been reliably reported that at this time the mother exposes the eggs with her forelimbs, making it easy for the young to leave the nest. Each egg is opened by the young inside with the aid of a sharp "egg-tooth" on the tip of its snout which is used to make a slit in the shell. The egg-tooth is lost within a few days. Once out of the eggs the young make immediately for the water and for the first few days they may remain near the female, not feeding but surviving on the remains of the embryonic yolk sac. Newly hatched Estuarine Crocodiles are about a foot in length; at this stage their predators are many and the survival rate in their early years is very low.

The Fresh-water Crocodile, unlike the Estuarine Crocodile, breeds towards the end of the dry season, that is, from August to October.

The eggs, numbering up to about 25, are laid in a hole about 12 inches deep made in a sand bank. The eggs take about 8 weeks to hatch, so that they have usually hatched before water from the monsoonal rains floods the nesting sites. Again it has been reported that the female regularly attends the nest during incubation.

The Fresh-water Crocodile grows to more than 10 feet in length, but averages only about 6 feet. It is harmless to man, in that it is timid and inoffensive, but this is not to deny that it will savagely defend itself if attacked or wounded.

The Estuarine Crocodile, on the other hand, is feared as a man-eater throughout much of its range. Attacks are extremely rare in Australia, but in various parts of New Guinea and the Indo-Malayan Archipelago people are taken regularly, if infrequently.

Contrary to popular opinion there are no alligators in Australia, true alligators being found only in the Americas and in China. However, this chapter could hardly end without briefly answering the perennial question, "what is the difference between a crocodile and an alligator?" There are several differences, but the simplest and most obvious is that the fourth tooth in the lower jaw of a crocodile fits into a notch in the upper jaw and is still visible when the mouth is closed. In an alligator this tooth fits into a socket in the upper jaw and is normally not visible when the mouth is closed.

Plate 2. The Eastern Snake-necked Tortoise (*Chelodina longicollis*). [Photo Author]—Text overleaf.

TORTOISES and TURTLES

Families *Chelidae, Cheloniidae, Dermochelyidae*
and *Carettochelyidae*

TURTLES, tortoises and terrapins make up the
ancient order Chelonia. Unfortunately, as
common names these terms are given different
meanings in different parts of the world, but only
two are applied to chelonians in Australia. The
large, marine species with powerful flippers are
known as turtles, whereas the smaller forms
inhabiting rivers and lakes, and all of which
possess webbed, strongly-clawed feet, are called
tortoises.

TORTOISES

All Australian tortoises belong to the family
Chelidae, which in turn belongs to the group
known as the Pleurodira, or Side-necked Tortoises. In this group, which is found elsewhere
only in South America and Africa, the head
and neck are bent sideways so that they can
be completely or partly hidden beneath the
front edge of the shell. This is in sharp contrast
to the vertical, S-shaped bend with which most
of the world's chelonians retract their heads
beneath their shells.

About a dozen species of fresh-water tortoises
are currently recognised in Australia but, as
individual river systems often have distinctive
tortoise populations, just which forms should be
recognised as species is uncertain. Probably no
group of Australian reptiles is in greater need of
study.

Two basic groups are recognised, each with
roughly the same number of species. These are
the Short-necked Tortoises and the Long-necked
or Snake-necked Tortoises.

The rarest of the Short-necked group is the
Swamp Tortoise (*Pseudemydura umbrina*). Only
a handful of specimens are known, all of which
are from an area of only a few square miles near
Bullsbrook in Western Australia.

Three Short-necked Tortoises are common in
eastern Australia, and all are river rather than
swamp tortoises. The Macquarie Tortoise
(*Emydura macquarii*) and Krefft's Tortoise
(*Emydura krefftii*) (Plate 3) both have distinctive
yellow markings on the face. These markings
are usually absent in the Saw-toothed Tortoise
(*Elseya latisternum*), another river tortoise;
it is a large, bull-headed species.

The Snake-necked Tortoises, as their name
implies, have very long necks. When fully
extended the head and neck together are about
as long as the shell. The Common or Eastern
Snake-necked Tortoise of Eastern Australia
(*Chelodina longicollis*) (Plate 2) is typically a
swamp dweller. Its head and upper shell (the
carapace) are dark brown to black, while the
broad lower shell (the plastron) is yellow, though
each individual plate is edged with black. In the
Large River Tortoise (*Chelodina expansa*) the
lower shell is much narrower than the carapace
and the head is proportionately much wider and
flatter.

Relatively little is known of the habits of
tortoises in the wild. Most of their lives are spent
in the water, where they feed on aquatic animals
such as fish, molluscs, crustaceans, and insects,
and may occasionally take small quantities of
submerged or floating aquatic plants.

Tortoises may often be seen floating on the
surface of the water, basking in the sun. They
will also emerge from the water to bask, sometimes on the banks of swamps or streams, but
more often on to logs or boulders projecting
from the water.

Normally, tortoises come onto land only to

Plate 3. Head of a Krefft's Tortoise (*Emydura krefftii*) from north-western Queensland. [Photo Author]

lay their eggs, but they sometimes travel overland for reasons that are not fully understood. During periods of drought large numbers of tortoises will sometimes leave a drying swamp and move overland, presumably in search of a new and more permanent home. Rabbit-proof fences all too frequently act as death-traps for these migrating tortoises for, unable to pass through the fence, they wander back and forth until they die, either from heat, desiccation, or starvation.

However, wet weather often appears to stimulate the overland movement of large numbers of tortoises, in roughly the same direction, from large bodies of water which are not in any danger of drying out. Why these migrations take place is unknown.

In their breeding habits, most Australian tortoises are believed to follow a similar pattern. As in all chelonians (but unlike most other reptiles), the male has a single intromittant organ which is inserted into the cloaca of the female during mating. Mating takes place in the water, but whether it is preceded by complex mating displays as in many foreign species is not known. The female may generally be distinguished by her relatively deeper body and by her shorter tail.

The mating season varies from species to species; in *Chelodina expansa* it has recently been found that overwintering of the eggs occurs, but in most species the eggs hatch about 8 to 10 weeks after being laid.

The eggs are usually laid during, or just after, · rain, when the ground is soft and allows the egg cavity to be excavated more readily. The nest is usually made on the bank of a stream or swamp. Using the cupped hind feet alternately, the female digs a hole, several inches in diameter and up to 6 inches deep, in which she lays up to about 20 white oval or sausage-shaped eggs, which she then covers with soil.

Like many tortoises and turtles in other countries, the females of Australian species are believed to be able to store sperm from a single mating for up to several years. The stored sperm can then be used, if necessary, to fertilise several batches of eggs without the need for further matings.

How long do tortoises live? Reliable records are few, but indicate that a life span of 30–40 years is not exceptional.

TURTLES

Living sea-turtles belong to two families. The Luth or Leathery Turtle (*Dermochelys coriacea*) is placed in a family of its own, for unlike all other marine turtles its carapace consists of many small plates embedded in a tough, leathery skin. The backbone is not firmly attached to the carapace, in contrast to the other turtles, in which it is firmly welded to the bones of the carapace. The Luth is the largest of all living turtles, growing to a length of more than 8 feet and with a weight exceeding 1,500 lb. It is common in Australian seas but breeds only rarely in this country.

The other marine turtles, like the tortoises already described, have well-developed, bony "shells" covered by horny plates. Five kinds are found in Australian waters. The Green Turtle (*Chelonia mydas*) (Plate 4), the Loggerhead (*Caretta caretta*) and the Hawksbill (*Eretmochelys imbricata*) are common off Australia's tropical coastline, and are occasionally seen in seas off the southern states. The Pygmy Green Turtle or Flatback Turtle (*Chelonia depressa*) is known only from the coastal waters of northern Australia, where it is abundant in many areas. In

Plate 4. A Green Turtle (*Chelonia mydas*) in a coral pool at Heron Island, on the Great Barrier Reef. [Photo Author]

1969 the Pacific Ridley (*Lepidochelys olivacea*) was first recorded breeding on the coast of Arnhem Land.

With the exception of the Green Turtle (and possibly the Flatback Turtle) all species are carnivorous, feeding on fish and other marine animals. The adult Green Turtle is largely vegetarian and browses on various kinds of algae. Young Green Turtles however, are carnivorous like the adults of other species.

All the above turtles except the Leathery Turtle are known to breed along various parts of the northern coastline of Australia, and all species are essentially similar in their breeding habits. Mating takes place in the sea, apparently usually on the surface. The females later come ashore on sandy beaches to lay their eggs, usually at night and on a rising tide. The female slowly heaves herself up the beach, leaving a broad track in the sand, to a point well above high-tide mark. There she uses her broad fore and hind flippers to scoop out a wide, shallow depression; sometimes she will make several attempts before choosing the final site. When the depression is about 1 foot deep, the edges of the hind flippers are turned upwards to form cup-like scoops, and are used to dig a hole about 10–12 inches deep and 9 inches in diameter. Into this the eggs are laid, usually two or three at a time, until they number between 50 and 200; the eggs are round, varying from about 1–2 inches in diameter in different species, having large yolks and tough leathery shells. When first laid they have a small dent in one side; as the eggs develop an internal pressure is built up and the dent disappears. Once egg-laying is completed, which may take from 30 minutes to several hours, all four flippers are used to fill the nest. The sand is scattered so effectively that all traces of the nest are obliterated.

During the breeding season males may wait offshore to mate with the egg-laying females. Each female may nest five or six times during the egg-laying season, which in Great Barrier Reef waters extends from about October to March, but American studies have indicated that most females breed only once every two or three years.

The eggs take an average of about nine weeks to hatch, and during this incubation period they are subjected to numerous hazards. On the mainland foxes and dingoes are adept at finding the eggs. Aborigines too, relish the eggs, which are often located with a thin, pointed stick. This is thrust into the sand in the general vicinity of the nest; when it pierces the egg chamber the albumen from the eggs causes sand grains to adhere to the stick, indicating the presence of the eggs. The newly hatched turtles generally emerge at night and must run the gauntlet of predacious ghost crabs and other animals before they reach the sea. Virtually nothing is known of the life history of the turtle from the time it enters the sea as a hatchling until the adult female returns to land for egg-laying.

In 1969 the Pitted-shell Turtle (*Carettochelys insculpta*) of New Guinea was first recorded from Australia, and numbers of these turtles have since been seen in the Daly and Victoria Rivers in the Northern Territory. This turtle, the sole member of its distinctive family (Carettochelyidae), was previously thought to be confined to the rivers of southern New Guinea. *Carettochelys* is a large turtle, growing to more than thirty inches in length; it has a high-domed shell covered with skin, flippers like a sea-turtle, and a distinctive head with nostrils at the end of a fleshy proboscis-like snout. It lays about 15 round eggs in a hole dug in a muddy river bank towards the end of the dry season.

Plate 5. The Smooth Knob-tailed Gecko (*Nephrurus levis*). The specimen shown is from the Musgrave Ranges in South Australia. [Photo Author] —Text overleaf.

GECKOS

Family *Gekkonidae*

Geckos are nocturnal lizards, most of them only a few inches in length; they are generally rather soft-bodied flabby lizards with thin, scaly skin in which the individual scales lie alongside each other and do not overlap like those of many other lizards, or of snakes. The scales are often modified to form tubercles or spines, while in many species the skin of the belly is so transparent that the internal organs are clearly visible. About 50 different kinds of geckos are found in Australia and among them are included many with bizarre shapes and habits; although all of them are non-venomous (as are all Australian lizards) and harmless, their unusual appearance all too often results in their being loathed and feared by humans.

Australian geckos are almost exclusively nocturnal and their vision is well adapted to such a way of life. Their eyes are relatively large and the pupil, which in daylight is a narrow vertical slit, dilates to almost fill the eye in darkness. Although geckos are able to detect even the slightest movement at a considerable distance, they are apparently unable to identify an object or distinguish it from its surroundings unless it moves. Their eyes, like those of snakes, have no eyelids and are covered by a protective, transparent scale. To keep this clean a gecko uses its broad, flat tongue to wipe the eye periodically, an advantage not enjoyed by snakes.

Geckos, like most other small lizards, feed almost exclusively on insects, although occasionally spiders, centipedes, or even small lizards are eaten. Once it sees an insect a gecko will rush to within a short distance of it then slowly, one foot at a time, stalk it until within striking distance, when it lunges forward and grasps the insect in its jaws. This whole performance is reminiscent of a cat stalking its prey. Unfortunately the gecko's eyes are often bigger than its stomach, as witnessed by many a gecko struggling with a moth or beetle almost bigger than itself and which it has no chance of subduing, much less of swallowing.

A gecko's jaws are equipped with numerous short, fine teeth and although the prey is roughly crushed it is not chewed before being swallowed. Once caught, an insect is usually pounded against the nearest object – the ground, a tree or wall – by the gecko throwing its head from side to side. This performance is commonplace and can create quite a lot of noise; many a visitor to a country homestead has wondered at the strange knocking noises emanating from somewhere above his head.

Geckos, unlike most other Australian reptiles, rarely drink from an open body of water but generally lap water from dew, rain, or seepage. Most of their moisture needs are obtained from their food.

Another characteristic of Australian, as well as of most other geckos, is the ability to discard the tail and grow a new one in its place. This is not a haphazard affair, for when a gecko loses its tail it breaks at a definite point where there is a built-in weakness in the vertebral column. Once the original tail, which is supported by bony vertebrae, is lost, any new tail will have only a stiff rod of cartilage, or gristle, to support it, for the vertebrae cannot be regrown. The new tail rarely looks like the original for it lacks any spines and tubercles. The time taken for a new tail to grow seems to vary from about three to 12 months.

Plate 6. The Northern Leaf-tailed Gecko (*Phyllurus cornutus*) grows to nearly a foot in length and is the largest Australian gecko. It is a tree gecko found in rain-forest areas along the coast and ranges from central New South Wales to northern Queensland. [Photo Author]

Geckos' tails occur in an amazing variety of shapes and sizes, as can be seen from the plates. In many species the tail appears to be used as a food reservoir, the fatty tissue deposited in good seasons being used by the gecko during the winter, or in times of drought, when it is unable to find or catch enough food.

Many geckos, when alarmed or threatened, raise their tails in the air, turn them towards their enemy and wave them slowly back and forth. The tail, once broken off, will wriggle violently for some time as a result of muscular contractions. These two observations have led to the not unreasonable suggestion that many geckos use their tails as a decoy; in presenting the tail to an enemy in such a way as to make it the part most likely to be attacked, it is easily lost, and once broken its violent wriggling will divert a predator's attention while its owner makes good his escape. However not all geckos without their original tails have lost them in this way, for fights between geckos during the breeding season can account for many lost tails.

As in many other groups of Australian reptiles, species from the southern parts of Australia have a definite breeding season. Mating occurs typically from late September to December; mating displays have not yet been observed in Australian geckos although some display by the male probably occurs in most kinds. The male generally approaches the female from behind or from the side, sometimes gripping the skin of her flanks between his jaws. Once the first bite is made in this way he tries to move his grip to the skin on the top or sides of her neck and once this is done he manoeuvres his body alongside hers. If she is receptive she lifts her tail in an arc to make it easier for the male to bring his vent opposite hers. As in all lizards, and in snakes, the male has paired sex organs. Although these are often called hemipenes, each penis is independent of the other so that the one used in mating depends largely on the side from which he approaches the female. The duration of a mating, in the few Australian species in which it has been observed, appears to average between 10 and 15 minutes.

The time between mating and egg-laying is not accurately known but is believed to be about six to eight weeks. At that time the female seeks out a suitable site to deposit her eggs, usually numbering two but sometimes one, in a rock crevice, under a log, or beneath the bark on a tree. In some species, such as the Tree Dtella, the eggs have hard, brittle shells rather like those of birds' eggs. In other species, such as the Velvet Geckos of the genus *Oedura*, the eggs have tough, but soft, leathery shells. In southern Australia the eggs generally hatch about seven to 10 weeks after being laid.

The situation in the tropical parts of Australia is little known. In several species well-developed eggs have been found almost throughout the year, suggesting that there is no fixed breeding season. Similarly the time taken for the eggs to develop in these regions might well prove to be different from that taken in the south.

According to the shape and structure of their feet, Australian geckos can be broadly divided into two groups. In one of these the fingers and toes are long, slender, and bird-like, ending in sharp claws. In the other group the fingers and toes are flattened, with adhesive pads on their lower surfaces and often having a tiny claw, which can be retracted, in a groove between the pads at the tip of each finger and toe. The strongly-

Plate 7. The Northern Spiny-tailed Gecko (*Diplodactylus ciliaris*) using its tongue to clean its lidless eye. This method of cleaning the eyes is characteristic of all geckos and snake-lizards. [Photo S. Breeden]

clawed geckos tend to be ground-dwelling whereas those with adhesive pads tend to be arboreal, but there are many exceptions in both groups.

Most houses in the tropics and many in the inland of southern Australia support a small colony of geckos which emerge from their hiding place at night to feed on the insects attracted to the lights. These agile little lizards, which run freely up and down walls and across ceilings, belong to the group with adhesive pads, and most people are more familiar with this group than with the group of clawed geckos. Although it is popularly believed that the pads are sticky, this is not so; the pads have a very complex structure which is made up entirely of modified scales. Each pad consists of many hundreds of fine, hair-like scales which, under a microscope, look rather like the bristles of a brush. How these work is not fully understood, but it is believed that these fine "hairs" or "bristles" are pressed into microscopic irregularities in the surface over which the gecko is climbing, providing sufficient traction to allow the lizard to cling to surfaces which to all appearances are perfectly smooth. Whether the bristles are able to form a vacuum and in this way act as suction discs on really smooth surfaces has often been debated, but it is not borne out by observation.

Although geckos appear to be delicate and fragile, they are particularly plentiful in both variety and numbers in Australia's desert regions. They survive there largely because of their nocturnal habits, for they would be unable to withstand the intense heat and dryness during the day. Geckos avoid these conditions by resting in rock crevices, burrows, hollow logs,

or grassy thickets, emerging only at dusk to feed. These same homes that protect them from the daytime heat also protect them from the cold, for temperatures on winter nights in the desert can fall to more than 20° below freezing point. Any small lizard venturing into the open on such a night would quickly freeze to death. This means that many desert geckos are unable to forage for long periods during the winter and must rely on stores of body fat for their survival.

Most of the geckos inhabiting central Australia have distributions extending into the more arid parts of each of the surrounding states. One of the most interesting and bizarre of these is the Smooth Knob-tailed Gecko (*Nephrurus levis*) (Plate 5). Only a few inches in length and with a pattern of yellowish cross-bands on a rich purplish-brown ground colour, it has a small round knob on the end of its fat, carrot-shaped tail. The Smooth Knob-tailed Gecko is generally found by day in a burrow in the sand; this burrow is often one which has been abandoned by a Central Netted Dragon (*Amphibolurus nuchalis*) (see Plate 18) although occasionally the two lizards may share a burrow. The gecko, however, is quite capable of excavating its own burrow in the sand, usually to a depth of between 1 and 2 feet.

A close relative of the Smooth Knob-tailed Gecko is the Spiny Knob-tailed Gecko (*Nephrurus asper*). This gecko, whose body is covered with numerous rosettes of small tubercles and whose tail is even shorter than that of its relatives, tends to live in rocky rather than sandy areas and is found almost as far east as the coast of central Queensland.

Like many other species, these geckos, when alarmed, raise their bodies high on the tips of

24

Plate 8. The Barking Gecko (*Underwoodisaurus milii*) is one of the most common species found throughout the southern half of Australia. Growing to about 6 inches in length, it is a ground-dwelling gecko that is usually found under rocks or logs. [Photo Author]

their toes, inflate their bodies with air, and throw themselves forward an inch or so towards an aggressor while at the same time uttering a muted but explosive "bark" or squeak – a performance which makes even the most self-assured person a little wary. Nor is it all bluff, for most geckos will not hesitate to bite; and although their bites are harmless and virtually painless to a human, they rarely fail to produce the desired effect: the gecko is promptly released. Incidentally, the function of a Knob-tailed Gecko's "knob" is unknown.

Probably the most important plant in the lives of desert reptiles is the ubiquitous "spinifex" or porcupine grass (*Triodia*). This grass grows in clumps, each clump consisting of a relatively dense thicket of interlacing, outwardly projecting spines (Plate 10). Porcupine grass offers the only ground cover over vast areas of desert and each clump usually supports a small community of animals including numerous insects, reptiles, and often birds and small mammals. One of the most common geckos found in the porcupine grass and certainly one of the most attractive of Australian species, is the Jewelled Gecko (*Diplodactylus elderi*) (Plate 10). It grows to about 4 inches in length and is dark brown to black with numerous scattered cream or pearl-coloured tubercles. Like several other members of its genus it can exude a smelly, thick, treacle-like fluid from pores along its tail. The agility of this gecko in what appears to be an impenetrable thicket of grass spines is shown clearly in the plate.

Scattered throughout the desert regions of Australia are isolated mountain ranges, some, like the Musgrave Ranges in South Australia, rising to between 2,000 and 3,000 feet above the surrounding desert. Others hardly deserve the title "mountains", being little more than low rocky outcrops. Nevertheless each of these supports a population of reptiles which make their homes in rocky crevices or under loose slabs of rock on the hillsides. Two of the geckos most commonly found in these situations are the Spotted Dtella (*Gehyra punctata*), a 4-inch brown lizard with scattered light brown spots and broad adhesive pads, and the Marbled Velvet Gecko (*Oedura marmorata*), a larger species with bold blotches or cross-bands of yellow on its blue-black body. But whereas the Spotted Dtella or a close relative may be found in similar rocky habitats in areas as widely separated as south-western Australia and Cape York Peninsula, the Marbled Velvet Gecko in other parts of Australia changes its way of life and is almost invariably found under bark on trees. Why this basic change in its preferred habitat should take place in different parts of the country is little understood, but it is probably linked with the presence or absence of competing species and the range of habitats from which it can choose.

The Tree Dtella (*Gehyra variegata*) (Plate 9) is a close relative of the Spotted Dtella and is found from the arid centre of the continent to the open forests and woodlands to the east, north, and west. It, too, grows to only a few inches in length; it is grey with irregular black marblings and has broad pads on its feet. Like many other lizards living on trees, when disturbed the Dtella rushes to the side of the tree away from its possible enemy and spirals upwards around the trunk of the tree so as always to keep the trunk between itself and the intruder.

Probably one of the most unusual ways of life of any gecko is that of another Dtella which,

Plate 9. The Tree Dtella (*Gehyra variegata*). [Photo Author]

throughout many parts of inland Australia, spends its life within the maze of tunnels in the enormous mounds of certain species of termites. In some places these mounds may be up to 15 feet high and 10 feet or more in diameter, and their outside surfaces are sometimes plastered with the droppings of the geckos which live inside, but which emerge at night to feed.

In the Tanami Desert in the Northern Territory I have taken more than 50 geckos from a small mound made by the termite *Nasutitermes.* The tunnels of the mound were filled with the gecko's eggs; some had long since hatched while others contained living embryos. Still other unhatched eggs contained dried-up embryos which indicated that quite a high proportion of the eggs, though fertile, fail to hatch. The geckos themselves are a source of food for a small python (*Liasis perthensis*) and for small carnivorous marsupials which also make their homes in the termite mounds.

Some of the geckos found in our arid regions are not entirely restricted to such a harsh environment and many species are as much at home in the dense wet coastal forests as they are in the arid interior. The Wood Gecko (*Diplodactylus vittatus*) occurs through much of southern Australia (except Tasmania). It is dark brown, with a light brown zigzag line along the centre of its back. In forested parts of the country it is usually found under stones or logs on moist soil, or in rotting logs and tree stumps. Often known as a Wood Adder, this harmless lizard is all too frequently killed because of its name.

A close relative of the Wood Gecko and surely one of the most beautiful of all Australian species, is the Golden-tailed Gecko (*Diplodactylus taenicauda*). This tree-living gecko is found only in a small area of savannah woodland in south-eastern Queensland, especially along the Condamine River and its tributaries. It is more or less black above with a fine network of grey, and has a bright orange or rust-coloured band along the length of the tail. As its habitat extends well beyond this part of Queensland the reasons for its restricted distribution are unknown. As happens so often in the study of Australian reptiles even the basic factors determining a species' distribution are rarely understood.

One of the most adaptable of Australian lizards is the little ground-dwelling Bynoe's Gecko (*Heteronotia binoei*), for it is as likely to be met in the arid interior as in coastal forests, from one end of the continent to the other. Only 3 or 4 inches long with small claws, it is very variable in colour; the ground colour is usually of the same basic shade as the soil or rocks among which it lives, while its back is covered with small black and yellow tubercles arranged in irregular cross-bands (Frontispiece).

Along the coast of New South Wales one of the most common species is the Southern Leaf-tailed Gecko (*Phyllurus platurus*). It is most plentiful in sandstone areas, where it lives under rocks, in crevices, and in small wind-blown caves. It is grey or grey-brown above with numerous tubercles which give it a prickly appearance; its head is more or less diamond-shaped while its tail is flat and spade- or heart-shaped. It is one of the most vocal of Australian geckos and when disturbed will sometimes utter a prolonged scream that could easily pass for the cry of a human baby. Unlike many other geckos it has managed to survive even in built-up suburban areas where its occasional appearance in house or garage causes much consternation.

28

Plate 10. The Jewelled Gecko (*Diplodactylus elderi*) in a thicket of porcupine grass. [Photo Author]

Two other geckos are found commonly in the same rocky environment in eastern Australia. One, Lesueur's Velvet Gecko (*Oedura lesueurii lesueurii*) is a soft, small grey species found along the coast and ranges of the south-eastern parts of the continent while the other, Tryon's Velvet Gecko (*Oedura tryoni*), is found more often in granite than sandstone areas, from northern New South Wales to north Queensland. It is typically a rich brown in colour with scattered whitish or yellowish spots.

The rich rain-forest areas of north-eastern Queensland are the homes of two exotic and beautiful geckos. De Vis' Banded Gecko (*Cyrtodactylus louisiadensis*) which also occurs in New Guinea, grows to nearly a foot in length and is light fawn with about six dark brown bands across its body. Its tail, especially in the young, is banded with white and dark brown. The Chameleon Gecko (*Carphodactylus laevis*) grows to about 9 inches and is rich reddish-brown with scattered dark brown spots, the tail being darker brown with four or five narrow white bands. The body and tail are vertically flattened.

One of the most interesting groups of geckos are those which exude a toxic, treacle-like fluid from pores along their bodies and tails. Two, the Golden-tailed Gecko and the Jewelled Gecko have already been mentioned. The remainder are all rather similar to one another, being grey above with irregular darker markings.

Probably the most bizarre of this group is the Northern Spiny-tailed Gecko (*Diplodactylus ciliaris*) (Plate 7), from the northern parts of Western Australia and the Northern Territory. It grows to about 6 inches in length and its tail has two rows of long, backward-directed spines, one on each side of the tail. Several more spines stick up over each eyelid. In two of its common southern relatives, the Western Spiny-tail (*Diplodactylus spinigerus*) from Western Australia and the Eastern Spiny-tail (*Diplodactylus intermedius*) from central and eastern Australia, the tail "spines" are little more than blunt tubercles.

Little is known of the origin or structure of the fluid exuded by these geckos. Its function is not fully understood but it may be defensive, for it has an unpleasant smell and is known to cause great discomfort if it gets into an eye or open wound. Intriguing habits such as this make geckos one of the most potentially exciting groups of reptiles to be studied in Australia.

Plate 11. The Robust Velvet Gecko (*Oedura robusta*) is a tree gecko found most commonly along the western slopes of the ranges and inland throughout northern New South Wales and southern Queensland. It is also known in south-western Australia. [Photo Author]

SNAKE-LIZARDS

Family *Pygopodidae*

THIS is the only group of reptiles whose members are found exclusively in the Australasian region. Nearly thirty species are known and with the exception of two that are found in New Guinea all are restricted to continental Australia. None are known in Tasmania.

The origins of snake-lizards are obscure but as they are restricted to the Australasian region, it is generally assumed that they evolved in this part of the world. There is no doubt that they evolved from an ancestor with normal limbs, for all species still retain, to some degree, remnants of limb structures.

Superficially the snake-lizards are so similar to snakes that they are nearly always feared and killed as snakes. All traces of forelegs have been lost while the hind legs have been reduced in all species until they are so small that they no longer play a part in locomotion. For this reason the snake-lizards have resorted to a snakelike movement which, of course, heightens their resemblance to snakes; by pressing the curves of their bodies against irregularities on the ground they literally "push" their bodies forward.

Because the hind limbs in some species are visible as small, scaly flaps these lizards are often called the flap-footed or scaly-footed lizards. Within these flaps are small bones which are the vestiges of the normal bones of a hind limb. The flaps are usually held flat along the side of the body and so are not readily seen. The largest flaps are found in the scaly-foots, *Pygopus* and *Delma*. In these, a complete set of miniature leg-bones and four toes are found, although this complex internal structure is not apparent from the outside. At times, especially when handled or injured, the flaps are held out at right angles to the body, rather like tiny wings. This has helped to give rise to the common belief in the Australian outback that some snakes have legs.

In other groups of snake-lizards the flaps are smaller and less conspicuous, and have fewer bones. One of these, and undoubtedly the most common and widespread of all species, is Burton's Snake-lizard (*Lialis burtonis*) (Plate 12), sometimes also called the Sharp-snouted Snake-lizard. It is a remarkably adaptable lizard which is as likely to be met in the spinifex desert of central Australia as in the coastal forests and savannahs or the rich lowland rain-forests of New Guinea. Indeed, there is hardly any part of Australia in which it is not found (except Tasmania). With its sharply angular, wedge-shaped snout it is unlike any other Australian snake-lizard. It is so variable in colour and pattern however, that anyone would be excused for believing that far more than a single species was involved. Sometimes it is almost a uniform brown, fawn, grey, or olive, but more often has up to eight darker brown stripes running along its body (including the belly) from head to tail. Each scale between these stripes may have one or more small black spots, while the stripes themselves may be broken up into spots or dashes. Differences in the intensity of these colours and markings produce a variety of patterns which do not follow any apparent geographic trends in their occurrence.

A close relative of Burton's Snake-lizard is Jicar's Snake-lizard (*Lialis jicari*) of New Guinea. The two are very similar in appearance and are found together in many parts of New Guinea. They offer an example of species that have reached New Guinea from Australia at different times in geological history, probably via temporary land connections between the two countries (see pp. 6-7).

Despite the commonness of Burton's Snake-

Plate 12. Burton's Snake-Lizard (*Lialis burtonis*) is found throughout many parts of Australia and New Guinea. This specimen, from the Northern Territory coast, shows one of the brighter colour patterns to be found in this variable lizard. [Photo Author]

lizard surprisingly little is known of its habits. It appears, like so many other snake-lizards, to be a ground dweller that lives among grass tussocks, rocks, and leaf-litter, where it sometimes feeds on insects but more often on small lizards. It is often seen to dart out from a clump of grass to catch a passing skink, and it appears that this habit of lying in wait for passing lizards is common. Although it is usually seen during the day, it is sometimes active at night. On several occasions I have followed a "snake" track made at night in the desert sand only to find a Burton's Snake-lizard sheltering under a clump of grass.

Although not found over such a wide area as Burton's Snake-lizard, Keeled Scaly-foots (*Pygopus*) are nevertheless common in many parts of Australia. These have rounded snouts and, as already mentioned, flipper-like hind limb flaps. In all but one form the keeled scales give the skin a rough appearance. The colour and markings are very variable, the ground colour ranging from various shades of grey and brown to olive and, in the young of some desert populations, pink. Dark body-markings, in the form of stripes or rows of spots, are sometimes present. The Common Scaly-foot (*Pygopus lepidopodus*) is common in coastal areas and differs from the Western Scaly-foot (*Pygopus nigriceps*) (Plate 13) in lacking a blackish mask over the head and neck.

Even less known, though fairly plentiful throughout Australia, are the Smooth Scaly-foots (*Delma*). Like the Keeled Scaly-foots they have relatively large hind limb flaps, but their scales are smooth. They are believed to be rather like the Keeled Scaly-foots in their habits but, in the central parts of Australia at least, are largely nocturnal.

Another group of snake-lizards are the so-called Worm Lizards (*Aprasia*), of which there are about nine species all rather alike in habits and appearance. They are small, burrowing, worm-like lizards without ear-openings and with hind limb flaps that are so small as to be scarcely visible. They rarely grow to more than about 6 inches in length, whereas most other snake-lizards reach adult size at between 1 and 2 feet. Worm Lizards are found only in southern Australia.

One or two snake-lizards are among the rarest of Australian reptiles. Only a few specimens of the Slender Snake-lizard (*Pletholox gracilis*) are known from a small area near Perth in Western Australia, while the Snake-headed Lizard (*Ophidiocephalus taeniatus*) is known only from a single specimen found at Charlotte Waters in South Australia in 1896.

So far as I am aware mating has never been observed in any snake-lizard. Like other lizards, and snakes, the sex organs of the male are paired, and mating is presumably similar to that in snakes. All species lay eggs which are rather elongated and have parchment-like shells.

Most species feed on insects, although, as already mentioned, some will eat small lizards. Water is drunk by lapping with a rapidly flickering tongue. Many species have a voice similar to that of geckos; it is usually a soft squeak or "bark" when the lizard is alarmed, although Burton's Snake-lizard sometimes emits a longer, drawn-out note.

If snake-lizards so closely resemble snakes, what then are the differences between the two? The similarity is largely external, for internally the structure of snake-lizards is only a slight modification of the basic lizard structure. In visible features there are several obvious differences between snake-lizards and snakes.

The most obvious of course, are the remnants

Plate 13. The Western Scaly-foot (*Pygopus nigriceps*) is found throughout the drier inland areas of Australia. [Photo Author]

of the hind limbs, which have already been described. Except for the "spurs" of some pythons (p. 78) no snakes have any structures resembling the feet of the snake-lizards. Whereas a snake's tongue is long, slender and forked, that of a snake-lizard is short, broad and fleshy, with a simple notch at its end. In most snake-lizards there are distinct ear-openings, one on either side of the head a short distance behind the eyes. These are lacking in snakes, whose hearing mechanism depends more on ground vibrations than on airborne sounds.

A snake's tail is very much shorter than its body and if any part of it is broken off it cannot be regrown. A snake-lizard's tail, however, is typically at least as long as its body, and like the tail of many other lizards is readily broken. Once broken, a new tail quickly grows from the stump of the old one and, although as in geckos the new one is supported only by a central rod of cartilage and is different in appearance from the original one, it can nevertheless grow to a considerable length.

In none of the snake-lizards are the belly scales so broad and distinct as in most snakes.

Although the snake-lizards are so unlike any other Australian lizards (except perhaps for some of the burrowing skinks), surprisingly enough they are more closely related to geckos than to any other group of reptiles. This relationship can be seen in some minor features – for example, both are vocal and both lack eyelids and have the habit of cleaning the eye spectacle with the tongue – but the vast differences in their appearance belie the fact that these two groups are derived from a common ancestor.

Plate 14. The Spinifex Snake-lizard *(Delma nasuta)* grows to about 15 inches in length. It is especially common in the porcupine grass (often called "spinifex") of central Australia. [Photo Author]

DRAGONS

Family *Agamidae*

ALTHOUGH this family of lizards is widely distributed from Australia through Indo-Malaysia, Asia, and southern Europe to Africa, few countries are as richly endowed with dragons as is Australia.

Dragons typically have dull, rough scales which lie side by side, instead of overlapping like those of snake-lizards or skinks. Many have spines and tubercles scattered over their bodies, while their claws are long, sharp, and bird-like. Although their tails are sometimes fragile and easily broken, regeneration occurs infrequently and then only poorly.

Whereas the teeth of most lizards are relatively uniform in shape and structure, those of dragons are often strongly differentiated. This is most marked in the larger species, in which enlarged "canine" and "incisor" teeth are developed in the front of the mouth.

The lining of the mouth is brightly coloured in some species. In the Bearded Dragon (*Amphibolurus vitticeps*) (Plate 20) and the Jacky Lizard (*Amphibolurus muricatus*) it is bright yellow, and is believed to have the function of scaring a potential enemy. When confronted by an aggressor these lizards open their mouths wide to present a sudden expanse of vivid colour.

Most moderate-sized dragons feed on a wide variety of insects and spiders. Many smaller species, especially in desert regions, subsist almost exclusively on ants, for these are not only the most abundant form of insect life in such regions but also supply much-needed water to the lizards that eat them. Large dragons, on the other hand, tend to be much less selective in their diets, and their food ranges from small mammals, nestling birds, and large insects, to various wildflowers.

It has already been explained in the Introduction how it is possible to show, with a reasonable degree of certainty, that the ancestors of some components of our fauna arrived in this country at an earlier time in geological history than the ancestors of other components.

This sequence is particularly obvious in our agamid lizards, for the 40-odd existing species in Australia fall into at least four distinct groups, each of which probably represents a distinct evolutionary line. Two of these groups are apparently relatively recent arrivals in this country, while the other two, which contain the bulk of Australian dragon species, have had a long evolutionary history in Australia. Whereas the more recent arrivals are restricted to the wetter coastal parts of eastern and northern Australia, the older elements of our dragon fauna are most plentiful in the dry and arid parts of the continent.

The most specialised and apparently the most ancient of these older groups is now represented by a single species, the Thorny or Mountain Devil (*Moloch horridus*). This lizard (Plate 16) is surely one of the most unusual lizards in the world. It averages only about 6 inches in length and despite its fearsome appearance is perfectly harmless. Its jaws are weak, while its teeth have quite complex crowns which are used to crush the small ants on which it feeds. The Thorny Devil is found in the semi-arid and desert regions of Western Australia, South Australia, the Northern Territory, and south-western Queensland. It is slow in its movements, and even at top speed its gait is simply a comical waddle, the body held off the ground by the thin, angular legs.

The Thorny Devil has probably presented more problems (most of which remain un-

Plate 15. The Frilled Lizard (*Chlamydosaurus kingii*), showing the frill in its normal "resting" position. [Photo Author]

answered) to biologists than any other Australian lizard. It can be seen from the plate that a large thorny hump projects from the lizard's neck and biologists have long been curious about its function. It has been suggested that it is a store of fatty tissue on which the Devil can draw when food is scarce, but specimens starved in captivity rarely show any diminution in the size of their hump. On the other hand, when alarmed the Thorny Devil pulls its head protectively down between its front legs, leaving the head-like hump in the position normally occupied by the head itself. This habit has led to the suggestion that the hump is a false head used to divert a predator's attention from the real one, but as it is rare to see a *Moloch* with a damaged hump, it would appear that the primary function of the hump – if, indeed, it has one – is still unknown.

Another characteristic of the Thorny Devil is the ability of its skin to "absorb" water. If any part of the lizard is put in water, even no more than a leg or a foot, water quickly moves over the whole body, so that within a few seconds the lizard is quite wet. When this happens the lizard can often be seen moving its jaws, and recent studies have shown that the outer layer of the skin contains microscopic channels which draw up water by capillary action and that this water, when it reaches the lips, is swallowed. Although it was once believed that the skin itself absorbed moisture, it has now been shown that this is not so. Indeed, if it did, then it would probably be able to lose water just as readily, and this would obviously be a great disadvantage for a diurnal desert reptile.

A Thorny Devil will eat up to 1,000 or more ants at a single meal; usually it sits quietly beside a trail of ants, flicking the occasional ant into its mouth with its short tongue. Like all dragons, the Thorny Devil is active by day. Like all

dragons, too, it is egg-laying, the female depositing a clutch of about six to eight eggs in a small hole which she makes in sandy soil. Mating generally takes place in October or November, the eggs being laid by early January and the young hatching in February or March. This breeding cycle is common to most dragons in the southern parts of Australia, although in a number of species a second batch of eggs is laid in late February or early March. Apparently only a relatively small proportion of females in any particular dragon population produce two clutches of eggs in a season. Many dragons mature when much smaller than the average adult size. However, such small specimens produce a smaller number of eggs per clutch than do larger specimens.

Whether a distinct breeding season occurs in dragons from the tropical parts of Australia is not known, but a few scattered observations suggest that the dragons in our northern regions breed throughout the year.

By far the largest group of dragons is that which has had such a long history of evolution in this country that its origins are obscure. Its species are most plentiful in the arid or drier parts of the continent, although a number of them have adapted to such a wide range of environments that they may now be found from the wetter coastal areas to the driest parts of the interior.

The best-known of this group, not only because it is the largest and most unusual in appearance, but also because its likeness appears on our coinage, is the Frilled Lizard (*Chlamydosaurus kingii*) (Plate 15).

The Frilled Lizard earns its name from the enormous ruff or frill of skin around its throat. This frill normally lies in a series of folds along the neck and chest, but when the lizard is aroused

Plate 16. The Thorny or Mountain Devil (*Moloch horridus*). [Photo Author]

the frill is raised. The simple action of opening the mouth causes the frill to be raised, for long extensions of the hyoid bones in the tongue run back into the frill and support it; the wider the mouth is opened the more the frill stands out from the neck.

Just as the purpose of the *Moloch*'s hump is uncertain, so too is that of the Frilled Lizard's frill. The most plausible suggestion is that the raised frill increases the apparent size of the head, and in this way presents a more formidable appearance to enemies. However, as the frill is well supplied with small blood-vessels it seems possible that it might play some part in the body's heat regulation, although there is as yet no evidence to support this suggestion.

Dragons, like other reptiles, are said to be "cold blooded", that is, their body temperatures cannot be regulated internally like those of birds and mammals, and fluctuate according to the temperature of their surroundings. As many dragons are active under conditions where temperatures are so high that the lizards would quickly die if their body temperature rose to that of their surroundings, many of the smaller dragons have adopted patterns of behaviour which help to keep their body temperatures up to 20° or more below that of their surroundings. These patterns include standing on the tips of their toes and raising their bodies and tails off the ground, in this way keeping an insulating layer of air between their bodies and the hot sand. Most desert lizards have pure white bellies which also serve to reflect heat radiated from the ground. If the lizards become too hot they will sometimes pant, like a dog, to reduce their temperature, or seek out cooler, shady spots.

Another means of avoiding excessive heat is the keeping of their bodies parallel to the sun's rays, so that a minimum surface area is available for heat absorption. Conversely, in the early morning, when they wish to raise their body temperatures after a cold night, they lie with their bodies pressed against the warm sand, and at right angles to the sun's rays. To avoid the intense cold of a winter night in the desert, most dragons burrow into the sand, or shelter in well-insulated clumps of grass or in rock crevices.

Anyone who observes dragons for a short period will soon become aware of unusual patterns of individual behaviour. The most obvious of these are loosely termed "head-bobbing" and "arm-waving". Head-bobbing often occurs when a lizard is sitting high on a rock or stump; suddenly it will quickly raise and lower its head a number of times. Few studies have been made of head-bobbing in Australian lizards, but studies of lizards in other countries have usually shown that bobbing is associated with sexual behaviour, either courting or the establishment of territories. Most of the lizards studied have revealed that the number of "bobs" and their timing are more or less constant and distinctive for each individual species. Whether this will prove true for most Australian species remains to be seen, but in some species bobbing seems to occur in both sexes throughout the year.

It has also been suggested that head-bobbing, by moving objects in relation to one another within the lizard's field of vision, permits it to identify various objects and to gauge distances. In those species in which the males have distinctive patches of colour on the throat and chest, head-bobbing may also help an individual to recognise the sex of other lizards in the area.

Arm-waving is also common in many Australian dragons. Although it sometimes takes place when a lizard is sitting quietly, it more often

Plate 17. Boyd's Angle-headed Dragon (*Gonocephalus boydii*) grows to nearly 2 feet in length. It is a tree-climbing lizard found only in the rain-forest areas of northern Queensland. [Photo Author]

occurs after a spurt of activity. The lizard will dash forward, stop suddenly, then wave one or other of its arms for a second or two, as if waving goodbye. If a dragon waves its arms while sitting quietly, the waving is generally much slower than that taking place after activity. In most of the species in which arm-waving has been observed, both sexes exhibit the behaviour.

The courting behaviour of most Australian dragons is largely unknown. One of the most unusual is that of the small Mallee Dragon (*Amphibolurus fordi*), for in this species, at least in New South Wales, courtship behaviour is almost the sole preserve of the females. During the mating season the females react to the presence of a male by raising their hindquarters high off the ground, while the tail is held in a long, high arc. The females orient their bodies so that the anal region is always facing the male, and if the male moves away then the female will often follow him, always holding her body in the same pose. An interested male will rush up to the female and "taste" her hindquarters. Whether the female's behaviour constitutes acceptance or rejection of the male is not known with certainty. In this species males are not territorial, and many males may live in the same small area without fighting between themselves. Other, larger, species are believed to exhibit territoriality, the males defending their territories against invasion by males from nearby areas. However, few species have been studied in any detail. One would certainly expect such behaviour to be most pronounced in those species which exhibit marked differences in colour or pattern between the sexes.

Although various species of dragons are found in every major environment in Australia, there are few obvious adaptations to particular habitats, and although Australian dragons are rich in number and variety only a few of their characteristics can be clearly correlated with their particular ways of life.

The Lake Eyre Dragon (*Amphibolurus maculosus*), which spends its life scampering about the glaring white salt crust of the lake after which it is named, has long projecting scales from the edge of each eyelid which apparently act as sunshades to protect the eyes from the glare.

Many desert dragons have their eyelids so shaped that when closed, there is an opening at the rear of the lids. As these lizards live in sandy areas, any sand entering the eye is extruded through this opening by the pressure of the eyelids on the surface of the eye. Other dragons that burrow into sand have valvular nostrils which are distinctively shaped and located to prevent sand from clogging the nasal passages.

Among the most adaptable of Australian dragons are the Bearded Dragons or Jew Lizards of the *Amphibolurus barbatus* complex. They are found roughly throughout the southern two-thirds of Australia, from the coastal regions to the arid centre.

Plate 18. The Central Netted Dragon (*Amphibolurus nuchalis*) is found commonly throughout the drier parts of all Australian States except Tasmania and Victoria. The specimen pictured is on a sandhill near the Mann Ranges in South Australia. [Photo Author]

As might be expected in such wide-ranging species, they are subject to considerable variation, with the ground cover tending to resemble the dominant colour in the environment. Coastal specimens, which live in low shrubs, or herbage, or on tree trunks, stumps, and fence posts, are predominantly grey, while those from the inland are richly flushed with ochrous yellows and browns. In Western Australia several small species of the Bearded Dragon have been described in which the "beard" is not so fully developed as in the larger eastern form. This is only to be expected, for the beard, like the frill of the Frilled Lizard, becomes proportionately larger as the lizard grows. The beard is hardly discernible in the newly hatched young of the Bearded Dragon, while hatchling Frilled Lizards have only a tiny fold of skin representing their future frill.

When annoyed or alarmed the Bearded Dragon inflates its body with air, opens its mouth and puffs out its spiny "beard" which, like the frill of the Frilled Lizard, is supported by extensions of the hyoid bones.

Bearded Dragons can often be seen early in the morning sunning themselves on the sun-warmed tarmac of a road. To increase the surface area of its body that can soak up the warmth from both road and sun, a lizard will flatten its body until it appears almost wafer thin. Unfortunately this attraction to roads leads to numerous deaths from speeding traffic.

Although skinks are the lizards predominantly seen in the wetter coastal regions, dragons predominate in the arid interior of the continent. In fine weather they can usually be seen darting from the shelter of one clump of porcupine grass to another, or dropping from sight from a rocky perch. Probably the most common species is the Central Netted Dragon (*Amphibolurus nuchalis*).

The Central Netted Dragon (Plate 18) makes a short and rather shallow tunnel in the sand, usually at the foot of a rock, termite mound, stump, mound of sand, or any other object which provides it with a vantage point from which it can survey the surrounding area. The dragon is usually to be seen on its perch, even in the very hottest part of a summer's day, from which it makes forays to catch passing insects. At the least sign of danger it drops down into its burrow. Like other dragons it lays eggs, and about four or five are laid in a specially constructed burrow which the female fills in with sand after the eggs are laid. In the south and south-west of Australia is found the Western Netted Dragon (*Amphibolurus reticulatus*) a species which is similar in appearance and habits to the blunt-headed Central Netted Dragon.

Among the porcupine grass sand flats of central, South and Western Australia the common dragon is the Military Dragon (*Amphibolurus isolepis*), a handsome reddish-brown species with rows of black spots down either side of its back, and yellowish lines, one along each side of the back and another along each side. Between these lines on each side is a broad dark band which extends almost along the length of the tail. Underneath, the Military Dragon is white, except for a large black patch on the throat and chest in mature males.

Across the drier parts of northern Australia, wherever mountain ranges or even small rocky outcrops occur, is found the Ring-tailed Dragon (*Amphibolurus caudicinctus*). Its ground colour usually matches closely the colour of the rocks on which it lives, while small light or dark coloured spots form irregular bands across the body. The tail is usually ringed with narrow dark brown or black bands.

Another common member of the genus *Amphibolurus* is the Ornate Dragon (*Amphibolurus*

Plate 19. The Eastern Water Dragon (*Physignathus lesueurii*). [Photo Author]

ornatus), a chunky-headed species, typically with irregular yellow blotches on a black body and with a series of alternate black and yellow bands on its flattened tail. The Ornate Dragon is common throughout many parts of south-western Australia.

In South Australia, in rocky areas, are two similar and closely related species, *Amphibolurus fionni* and *Amphibolurus decresii*. Females of both species are rather dull brown with irregular darker markings, especially along the flanks. Males, on the other hand, are much more colourful; they are usually blue-black above with bright yellow markings, while their throats are striped with black, blue, yellow, and orange bands.

Throughout the tropical north and north-east of Australia is the most common representative of another genus of dragons. The Two-lined Dragon (*Diporiphora bilineata*) (Plate 21) grows to only about 7 or 8 inches, at least two-thirds of which are tail. The colour is very variable, from almost uniform pale brown to dark reddish-brown, with or without two or three white lines along the back and irregular or broken black cross-bands.

Another major group is termed "Earless" Dragons, because their ear-openings are completely covered by scales. All are small, rough-scaled dragons averaging only a few inches in length, and rather heavily-built in relation to their size. Earless Dragons are found in the drier parts of all states.

Finally, our more recent migrants are almost entirely restricted to the eastern coastal and near coastal areas. The Eastern Water Dragon (*Physignathus lesueurii*) is shown in Plate 19. It grows to more than 3 feet in length, and it inhabits creeks and rivers from north Queensland to Victoria. Its favourite haunts are the she-oaks and other trees overhanging the water, into which it will drop and stay submerged when danger threatens. Adults of both males and females may be bright red on the belly. The eggs are normally laid at the end of a tunnel made in the bank of a stream.

Even more recent migrants from New Guinea are several species of Angle-headed Dragons, one of which, *Gonocephalus boydii*, is shown in Plate 17. All are found in the patches of rain and wet sclerophyll forest along the coast and ranges of Queensland and New South Wales.

Plate 20. The Inland Bearded Dragon (*Amphibolurus vitticeps*). This specimen is from central Australia, Mt Olga being visible in the background. [Photo Author]

GOANNAS OR MONITOR LIZARDS

Family *Varanidae*

FEW REPTILES have become as prominent in their country's language and folklore as the Australian goanna, for the number of bushmen's yarns about it are legion.

It is generally agreed that the word goanna is a corruption of the name iguana, which was applied by the early settlers to this and to other groups of lizards because of their supposed likeness to the true iguanas of the Americas, (and which also occur in Madagascar, Tonga and Fiji). However the uniquely Australian name goanna is now firmly established in our language and is used only for the members of this family, which in other countries (and sometimes in Australia) are generally called "monitor lizards".

Of the world's 25 or so species of goannas, which are found in various parts of Africa, Asia, the Indo-Malayan Archipelago, New Guinea, and Australia, nearly 20 are currently recognised as occurring on the Australian continent, and of this 20 at least 15 are found nowhere but in Australia. All living members of the family belong to the genus *Varanus*, which includes the largest lizards living in the world today.

Except for Tasmania, goannas are found throughout Australia and have evolved adaptations to a great range of environments. Although these adaptations are reflected in their appearance, goannas are nevertheless remarkably similar to one another in most features. All are powerfully built, with strong limbs equipped with long, sharp, curved claws. The head is rather pointed and wedge-shaped, while the tail, though typically long and slender, is muscular and powerful. Unlike that of a gecko, snake-lizard, or skink, the tail of a goanna cannot be regrown if broken. The body is usually rather slender but old specimens are often found with enormous girths due to layers of fat in the body wall. The skin is tough and leathery, with the scales lying up against one another instead of overlapping like those of some other lizards and most snakes. Old specimens are often heavily scarred, possibly as a result of fighting during the breeding season, for fights between rival males are apparently common.

As befits such a predatory reptile the numerous teeth are long, sharp and backwardly curved, making it difficult for prey to escape once caught in the powerful jaws. Food is not chewed, but swallowed whole or in pieces, being torn apart by the combined efforts of the teeth, forelimbs,

Plate 21. A Two-lined Dragon (*Diporiphora bilineata*) from coastal sand dunes in the Northern Territory. [Photo Author]

and sometimes even the hind limbs. Although they are typically hunters, with a varied diet that includes insects, lizards, snakes, birds, and mammals, goannas will readily feed on carrion. In sheepfarming areas it is not uncommon to see several goannas feeding from a dead sheep, and they are sometimes blamed unjustly for its death.

It is probably this liking for carrion that has given rise to what is probably the most widely believed myth about any Australian reptile – that a wound caused by the bite of a goanna is incurable, breaking out afresh every year; or, as in another version, every seven years! It is simply that when a goanna bites, the decaying food and bacteria in its mouth can readily cause a prolonged and troublesome infection. Provided that a bite is treated with a mild antiseptic, little trouble should be experienced; the same can be said of the bites of other lizards.

Because of the snake-eating habits of some species (which often result in fierce battles between goanna and snake), it has been said that goannas are immune to snake venom. Another version of this supposed immunity has them rushing off after such an encounter to feed on some legendary plant which in turn neutralises the effects of the venom. This bush yarn was put to good use by Banjo Paterson in "Johnson's Antidote", an amusing poem which should be compulsory reading for all aspiring herpetologists! Others, with less poetical and more mercenary turns of mind, have cashed in on this legend to sell various goanna-derived preparations as patent snake-bite cures. Fortunately the incidence of snake-bite in Australia is so low that few people have found it necessary to test the effectiveness of these cures.

Another myth concerns the properties of goanna fat or oil. Believed to have amazing powers of penetration (even passing through glass!) and to be a cure-all for everything from toothache to lumbago, it is still being offered for sale in Australia. Alas, its effects are psychological rather than physical.

Most members of this family of lizards are terrestrial, or ground-dwelling, in their habits. Included in this group is the most common and widely ranging of all Australian goannas, the

Plate 22. The Perentie (*Varanus giganteus*). This rocky hill clothed in porcupine grass is in the Musgrave Ranges in South Australia, and is a typical habitat of the Perentie. [Photo Author]

Sand or Ground Goanna (*Varanus gouldii*), a species found throughout the continent, from the deserts to the wetter coastal areas. Its colour and pattern vary greatly, ranging from almost black in south-western Australia to the brightly-coloured desert form (Plate 24). The most consistent markings are the light-coloured tip to the tail and a dark streak, edged above and below with white, from the eye to the neck. The Sand Goanna may grow to nearly 5 feet but averages only 3 to 4 feet.

When necessary it can run very fast to escape its enemies; it rarely has to run far, however, as it generally keeps within a relatively short distance of cover. In forested areas its home is usually a hollow log or stump but in open country it digs a burrow. The entrance is permanently open and though the burrow may be up to 3 feet deep, the closed end is usually only an inch or two below the surface. Then if the main entrance is closed off or an enemy follows the goanna into its burrow, a few scrapes with its feet will let the goanna escape through the closed end. As might be expected, rabbit warrens are a favourite haunt of Sand Goannas, for they provide both food and ready-made shelter.

The largest of all Australian goannas is the Perentie (*Varanus giganteus*) (Plate 22), a species growing to a length of between 7 and 8 feet. Found in the arid regions of central and western Australia, it generally makes its home in the isolated rocky outcrops or mountain ranges scattered across the desert countryside. Although the Perentie will make foraging trips into the surrounding sandhills it rarely travels very far from its rocky retreat; however in some areas, especially in Western Australia, it frequently lives in trees.

Other goannas make their homes in rocky hills and mountain ranges, where they live in crevices and among tumbled boulders. One small species, less than 2 feet in length, has marked adaptations to the rocky environment. It is the Spiny-tailed Goanna (*Varanus acanthurus*) (Plate 25), a reddish-coloured species from the northern half of Australia. Its tail is covered with strong, blunt, backward-directed spines; if an attempt is made to dislodge the

Plate 23. Two newly hatched young of the Lace Monitor (*Varanus varius*) from the Warrumbungle Mountains in New South Wales. The bright colour pattern displayed by these young normally becomes much duller with age. [Photo Author]

goanna from its rocky crevice it holds its tail in front of its body for protection, while the spines catch in irregularities in the rock, making it next to impossible to dislodge the lizard.

The Mangrove Goanna (*Varanus semiremex*), a 2-foot species with silvery-grey body and irregular dark spots, is found along the tropical north coast of Australia, especially in mangrove swamps or other coastal environments. It readily enters salty or brackish tidal waters and, in keeping with the rest of its habits, often feeds on small mud-crabs and fish.

Although most ground-living goannas tend to be rather small, averaging only about 2 feet in length, several of those from the arid parts of the continent attain an adult length of only 7 or 8 inches, and qualify for the title of "pygmy" goannas.

Of the arboreal or tree-living goannas, probably the best known is the Lace Monitor (*Varanus varius*) (Plate 23), a species found throughout many parts of eastern Australia. As it grows to a length of more than 6 feet, it is second in size only to the Perentie. The young (and some adults) are brightly banded with yellow and blue-black (as shown in the plate) but the pattern tends to break up with increasing age until the yellow is reduced to irregular spotting and banding.

Although the Lace Monitor is the best known of tree-goannas, it is not the most common. The Timor Tree Monitor (*Varanus timorensis*) is found over a large part of northern Australia; it averages only 2 feet in length, with a colour pattern of numerous bands of whitish rings on a blue-black ground colour. Similar in size but even more widely distributed, is the Mournful Tree Monitor (*Varanus tristis*); its common name is derived from its sombre blackish-brown colouring, although in some areas this colour is lightened by rows of small light-coloured rings. The Mournful Tree Monitor is found throughout the northern two-thirds of the continent, except for the eastern coast and ranges of New South Wales.

A picture of adaptations in this family of lizards is incomplete without mention of the Water Monitor (*Varanus mertensi*). This goanna is found in various rivers and lagoons in northern

Plate 24. A Sand Goanna (*Varanus gouldii*) from the Tanami Desert. [Photo Author]

Australia, from the Kimberleys through Arnhem Land and the Gulf Country to Cape York Peninsula. Its tail is compressed vertically to make an effective paddle when swimming. Its nostrils are on the top of its snout (instead of on the side as in most other species), and are equipped with small flaps of skin which act as valves to close off the air passages when the lizard is underwater. It can stay submerged for long periods of time. The Water Monitor feeds largely on fish and other aquatic animals. Incidentally, although most goannas rarely enter the water, they are all powerful swimmers.

Mating in goannas is essentially similar to that described earlier for other lizards. All are egg-layers, and at least in the southern parts of Australia there is a definite breeding season extending from about September to December, the eggs hatching between December and March. However, in New South Wales there have been authentic reports of hatchling goannas emerging from nests in early spring, which suggests that on at least some occasions, late summer matings result in eggs being laid late in autumn.

Although the breeding habits of most goannas are unknown and there is undoubtedly great variation in the number of eggs laid and the time they take to develop, the habits of the Lace Monitor are probably reasonably typical of goannas generally.

The Lace Monitor lays up to about 20 eggs which are rather elongated, with parchment-like shells, and averaging about 2 inches in length. These are laid in a hole made by the female at a depth of 6 to 12 inches. They are covered with soil and then take about eight to 10 weeks to develop. The young literally cut their way out of the egg with a sharp "egg tooth" on the tip of the snout; several slits may be made in the shell before the young goanna finally emerges. The young then make their way up through the soil, which may be partly softened by fluids from the broken eggs, and once emerged they are fierce predators, well able to take care of themselves. The egg tooth falls off soon after birth.

Although heat from the sun is usually sufficient to incubate the eggs, additional heat may be supplied, especially in forest areas where it is

Plate 25. The Spiny-tailed Goanna (*Varanus acanthurus*). The specimen pictured is from Mount Isa in Queensland. [Photo Author]

most required. After laying her eggs the female fills in the hole by raking into it soil, and often a considerable quantity of grass or leaf-litter, with her feet. As this vegetable matter decays in the following weeks, it generates heat which helps in the incubation of the eggs.

Not all goannas make a simple hole in which the eggs are laid. Some, like the Sand Goanna, may dig a tunnel, several feet long, at the end of which the eggs are laid and the tunnel then filled in.

A common and distinctive breeding habit of a number of goannas, including at times the Lace Monitor and the Sand Goanna, is that of using termite mounds as incubators for the eggs. The female makes a tunnel into the termite mound and there lays her eggs. After she leaves the nest, the termites immediately set to work to repair the damaged mound and within a relatively short time the eggs are sealed off from the outside. They can develop within the nest secure from most of their natural predators. Not only are they protected, but the temperature of the decaying material within the mound is much higher and more stable than that outside. In this way the termite mound both protects and incubates the eggs. It is generally believed that the young, when they hatch from the eggs, must then make their own way out of the termite mound. However, on several occasions when adult goannas have been disturbed at termite mounds, newborn young have been found emerging. This suggests that the female may remain near the nest until the young are ready to hatch, at which time she makes a new tunnel to release the young. If this is so then her performance is a remarkable one, for not only must she remember where the eggs are laid but she must also "know" when the eggs have hatched and the young are ready to emerge.

When moving at normal speed a goanna's gait can only be described as a rather comical waddle. The head and body are raised off the ground and slowly moved from side to side. The tongue, which is long, slender and forked, is wholly snake-like and, like that of a snake, is constantly flickering in and out when the goanna is on the move. This same waddling motion is also used

Plate 26. The Pygmy Mulga Goanna (*Varanus gilleni*), from central Australia, rarely grows to more than 18 inches in length. [Photo Author]

when running at speed; only if really hard pressed, and over relatively short distances, will a goanna fold its front legs flat against its body and run only on its hind legs. To get an occasional view of its surroundings when moving through long grass, a goanna will sometimes raise itself vertically by using its tail and hind legs as a tripod.

A large goanna at bay puts on an impressive display. The head and body are raised high off the ground, the body is inflated with air and the loose skin of the throat is expanded to make a dewlap. Instead of flickering in and out, the tongue is held out for long periods, quivering tensely. The tail is curved and whip-like, and is readily used to flay an opponent. The whole performance is accompanied by slow but violent hissing.

Plate 27. A South Australian specimen of the Shingle-back (*Trachydosaurus rugosus*). [Photo Author]

SKINKS

Family *Scincidae*

NEARLY 250 species of skinks are known from Australia, more species than in any other family of reptiles. They are so diverse in their appearance and habits that it is difficult to describe them in general terms. Most are sun-loving lizards with smooth shiny scales and slender bodies, but fat, rough-scaled forms are also plentiful. Some lay eggs while others bear live young. Although most skinks have four well-developed legs, each with five toes, loss of toes or even of limbs has occurred in the evolution of several groups, so that species with reduced numbers of toes or limbs are common in Australia. One or two are quite snake-like in appearance, having completely lost all four of their limbs. This degeneration of the limbs would seem to have occurred independently within different groups of skinks.

Because of this very diversity, it would be difficult to present a general discussion of such features as reproduction, adaptation, etc., and different groups of skinks have often found different ways of overcoming the same problem in their struggle to survive in various environments.

One feature common to nearly all skinks is their ability to break off and subsequently replace all or part of their tail. The advantages of this ability have already been discussed in the section on geckos. The reproduced tail takes some months to attain the length of the original and is supported by a rod of cartilage in place of the original bony vertebrae. The new tail is usually not the same in appearance as the original one; the scales tend to be more simple in structure, while the new colour and pattern are also less

complex. Especially common in skinks are multiple tails; as a result of a complete, or more often a partial break in the tail, regeneration may result in the formation of two, three or even four tail buds, which in turn develop into a veritable barrage of tails.

By far the most numerous of Australian skinks are the various species known by such common names as Fence Skinks, Garden Skinks, and Grass Skinks. All are small, averaging only about 4 inches in length, and are typically active, sun-loving lizards. These common names are good guides to the habits of many of these diminutive lizards, for various species are commonly seen scampering through grass and low vegetation, and are found around houses in both city and country areas.

Along the eastern seaboard of Australia two of the most common skinks of this group are the Grass Skink (*Leiolopisma guichenoti*) and the Fence Skink (*Leiolopisma delicata*). Both are light grey in colour with darker grey flecks on the back and a black stripe along each side of the body. The range of the Grass Skink extends throughout much of southern Australia. Also found across the southern half of Australia, including Tasmania, is the Three-lined Skink (*Leiolopisma trilineatum*). It is metallic bronze above, usually with three black, light-edged stripes along the back. The underside is silvery-cream and in some specimens the throat is flushed with bright red or pink. This colour does not appear to be related to either sex or season, and its function, if any, is not known.

Closely related to the small skinks described above are the Four-fingered Skinks, which as their group-name implies, have only four fingers on each of the front legs. They tend to be rather larger than the Grass and Garden Skinks, averaging 5 to 6 inches in length. They are most

Plate 28. The Copper-tailed Skink (*Ctenotus taeniolatus*). [Photo Author]

plentiful in northern Australia, where the Brown Four-fingered Skink (*Carlia fusca*) is probably the one most frequently seen. It is rather dull reddish-brown in colour. In New South Wales and Queensland is the related Rainbow Skink (*Carlia tetradactyla*), whose dull brown ground colour is often relieved by stripes of red, yellow, and blue along each side of its body.

All of these small skinks have a characteristic "window" in each of their lower eyelids. The window is an oval transparent or semi-transparent scale in the middle of the lower eyelid, and is seen only when the lizard's eyes are closed.

Another remarkable characteristic of these small skinks is the habit of the females of laying their eggs in communal nests. All species lay eggs, each female depositing a clutch of two or three eggs once or twice in a season. However nests containing from about 20 up to more than 200 eggs are often found. Although only three or four of the most common species are definitely known to lay in communal nests, it seems probable that related species will be found to have similar habits when their life histories become better known.

Although these small skinks are so common and easy to observe, surprisingly little is known about their habits. Several years ago, walking out into my garden just on dusk one warm November evening, there on the grass at my feet was a tumbling, twisting, squirming "ball" of more than 16 Grass Skinks, each individual skink having a firm grip with its jaws on another skink. After about five minutes they scattered in all directions. What were they doing and what was the purpose of the "ball"? Were they fighting? Mating? This single observation clearly illustrates the need for detailed study of even our more common reptiles.

Snake-eyed Skinks are so called because their eyes are covered by a single immoveable transparent scale, or spectacle, similar to that found in snakes. It has already been mentioned that in many skinks there is a transparent window in the lower eyelid, and the spectacle of a Snake-eyed Skink is believed to have evolved through the gradual enlargement of the "window" in the lower eyelid and the subsequent fusion of the lower with the upper eyelid.

Probably the best-known of this group is Bouton's Snake-eyed Skink (*Cryptoblepharus boutonii*) (Plate 30); this tiny, slender, 4-inch, sun-loving lizard is light silvery-grey with a dark grey stripe along each side, and is usually found on trees, fence-posts or around buildings in both city and country areas. Several subspecies of Bouton's Snake-eyed Skink have been described from Australia, most of which will probably prove to be species distinct from closely related forms which are regarded as races of species once occurring from the west coast of South America through the Pacific and Indian Oceans to Africa.

Although not the most common, probably the best known Australian skinks are the large, heavily built Blue-tongue Lizards, various species of which are found in almost every part of Australia, including Tasmania. Blue-tongue Lizards are frequently kept as pets, and live long and well in captivity on a mixed diet including snails, raw meat, egg, milk, bananas, and other fruits. Their common name refers to the light to deep blue tongue, which is slowly but constantly flicked in and out whenever they are alert or on the move. All are alike in build, having large, wedge-shaped heads, narrow necks, smooth-scaled broad, fat bodies (often exaggerated by their habit of inflating themselves with air when alarmed) and fairly short, thick, pointed tails. Their legs seem almost too small for their bodies, but they can move quite fast if hard pressed.

Plate 29. A Western Spiny-tailed Skink (*Egernia stokesii*) from the Macdonnell Ranges of central Australia. [Photo Author]

Generally, however, they tend to stand their ground and rely on bluff to save them from their enemies. With its body more or less in a semi-circle, its head held high and mouth agape, and hissing slowly, a Blue-tongue Lizard will turn itself quickly so as always to face its aggressor. An unwary finger or toe will be held in a truly vice-like grip, and no amount of pulling will free it without causing painful lacerations, for with each attempt to remove it the lizard tightens its grip. The rather blunt, conical, crushing teeth of these lizards are not as harmless as they might appear.

The Eastern Blue-tongue Lizard (*Tiliqua scincoides*) is shown in Plate 31. Although the young are strongly banded, these bands tend to break up in adults. Another banded species is the Western Blue-tongue (*Tiliqua occipitalis*) which is found throughout the southern arid interior of continental Australia. Its dark bands, and a conspicuous black stripe along the side of the head, stand out against the bright ochrous ground colours of yellow and reddish-brown.

In the south-eastern section of Australia, including Tasmania, is found the Southern, Blotched, or Highlands Blue-tongue (*Tiliqua nigrolutea*). Similar in build to those already described, it has a distinctive colour pattern of pink or orange blotches on a blue-black ground colour. Like the other blue-tongues, this species averages about 12 to 15 inches in length but occasionally approaches 2 feet.

Belonging to the same genus as the Blue-tongue Lizards, but very different in appearance, are several species of smooth, slender skinks. The Pink-tongue Skink (*Tiliqua gerrardii*) as its name implies, has a flesh-coloured tongue. It is generally fawn-coloured with numerous irregular dark cross-bands and its tail is very long, slender, and partly prehensile. The Pink-tongue Skink is found in the more densely forested parts of the coast and ranges of eastern Australia, from Cape York to Sydney. The Oak Skink (*Tiliqua casuarinae*) with its small legs and long, slender body and tail is quite snake-like in appearance. Its general ground colour is olive-brown, but black-edged scales form irregular cross-bands along the body and tail, while red, yellow, and black scales are scattered along its sides; the Oak Skink is found along the coast and ranges from northern New South Wales to Victoria and Tasmania. Its counterpart in south-western Australia is Gunther's Skink (*Tiliqua branchialis*), a lizard with a black-flecked brown body and often three conspicuous black spots on either side of the neck.

All of the Blue-tongue Lizards and their close relatives produce living young and although the average brood is from six to 12, some of the larger species occasionally produce up to 30 young. Whereas the Blue-tongues are active by day, their slender cousins like the Pink-tongue and the Oak Skink tend to be nocturnal in their habits. Insects, snails, and slugs make up the bulk of their diet, but all species are omnivorous to some extent and will sometimes be found eating fruits or carrion.

In the majority of live-bearing reptiles the young simply hatch from eggs within the body of the mother. However, in several of the Blue-tongue Lizards, and in a number of other live-bearing Australian skinks, it has been found that a type of placenta, resembling that found in some primitive mammals, is formed between the mother and the young. Such a placenta permits an exchange of food and waste products between the blood streams of the mother and the developing embryos.

The most bizarre of all Australian skinks is the Shingle-back Lizard (*Trachydosaurus rugosus*), whose unusual appearance is shown in Plate 27.

Plate 30. Bouton's Snake-eyed Skink (*Cryptoblepharus boutonii*) from coastal New South Wales. [Photo Author]

Also known as the Bobtail, Stumpy-tail, Double-headed Lizard, Pine-cone Lizard, and Boggi, this lizard is found throughout the drier parts of southern Australia, from about Bathurst in New South Wales to the coast of Western Australia. Unlike the prolific Blue-tongue Lizards, to which it is closely allied, the Shingle-back normally produces only two young at a time, though triplets are born occasionally. Growing to about 18 inches, the Shingle-back is a relatively slow-moving lizard which feeds on snails, slugs, carrion, native fruits and flowers. During the mating season, in October and November, it is a common sight on roads in western New South Wales to see a female Shingle-back ambling along, hotly pursued (if that is the right phrase!) by one, two, or three courting males. Little is known of mating and pre-mating displays in this or any other Australian skink, though scattered observations suggest that complex mating displays and territorial behaviour occur in some species.

The genus *Egernia* contains many species whose habits and appearances are so diverse that no collective name has ever been applied to them. Some, like White's Skink (*Egernia whitii*), are relatively smooth-scaled, medium-sized (averaging about 7 inches) lizards which are usually seen sunning themselves at the entrances to rock crevices. White's Skink, which is found in scattered localities across the southern half of the continent, generally has a distinctive yellow or white ring around each eye; the body colour is variable, but usually consists of light-coloured spots and bands on a dark-brown field.

There are several larger *Egernias* which also live in rocky areas, but which are more obviously adapted to the rocky environment than White's Skink. These, like the Spiny-tailed Goanna described in an earlier chapter, have their bodies and tails covered by large, strong, backward-directed spines which catch in irregularities in the rocky crevices in which the lizards shelter and make it virtually impossible to dislodge them from their retreats. Cunningham's Skink (*Egernia cunninghami*), which ranges from south-eastern Queensland to South Australia, is usually some shade of brown, liberally flecked with black and white. The tail is round and gradually tapers to a point, being proportionately rather like that of a conventional Blue-tongue. Common in rock outcrops in central, south and south-western Australia is the Western Spiny-tailed Skink (*Egernia stokesii*) whose tail is short and flattened, as shown clearly in Plate 29.

Another distinct group of *Egernias* are the desert burrowing species. The largest of these is Kintore's Skink (*Egernia kintorei*), which grows to nearly 18 inches in length. It is rich reddish-brown above, with delicate blue-grey sides and a white belly. Adult pairs of lizards construct complex burrow systems in the desert sand; these systems have several openings, and a number of blind tunnels, and the whole system may extend over a distance of 15 to 20 feet and be up to 3 or 4 feet deep. Until they mature the young will often share the burrows with their parents. Although the skinks may be seen sunning themselves at one of the entrances in the early morning or late afternoon, they appear to do most of their foraging at night. One interesting feature of this species is its habit of always defecating in the same spot, so that small piles of fecal pellets can be found near the burrow.

A much smaller burrowing species is Rosen's Skink (*Egernia inornata*). Growing to only 6 or 7 inches, individual skinks make small burrow systems in the sand, usually at the base of clumps of porcupine grass (*Triodia*). One entrance of the burrow almost invariably faces east, and

Plate 31. The Eastern Blue-tongue Lizard (*Tiliqua scincoides*). [Photo Author]

it is at this entrance that the skink can be seen sunning itself in the early morning, and from which it makes short dashes into the open to capture passing insects. One branch of its burrow ends only half an inch or so below the surface of the sand; if an attempt is made to dig the skink from its burrow it sits in this branch until, if it seems it will be caught, it breaks through the surface crust and makes its escape.

In the thickly forested coastal areas of New South Wales and Queensland are several large, relatively smooth-scaled *Egernias*. The Land Mullet (*Egernia major*) is a sleek, velvety-black or dark brown lizard which reaches a length of more than 2 feet, while the Forest Skink (*Egernia rugosa*) (Plate 33) of Queensland grows to about 18 inches in length and is rich brown in colour.

Only one other *Egernia* merits special attention. The Arboreal Skink (*Egernia striolata*), as its name implies, spends most of its life on trees, stumps, and even fence posts, where it hides in crevices or under bark. It reaches about 8 inches in length and is silvery-grey to brown with a series of fine, broken black lines along the centre of the back and a broad black stripe from the eye along each side of the body.

All of the *Egernias* produce living young, averaging about 2 to 4 to a litter, though some of the larger species may have up to a dozen young. All are carnivorous, feeding almost exclusively on insects and small lizards. In captivity some species have been known to eat fruit. In 1958, in the Warrumbungle Mountains, I caught the type specimen of a new species of *Egernia* when it rushed up to my feet to eat some raisins that had dropped from my lunch.

Like the members of the genus *Egernia*, the members of the genera *Ctenotus* and *Spheno-morphus* are also so numerous and variable in appearance that no collective common names have ever been coined for them. One group consists of medium-sized lizards, typically with colourful, striped bodies and tails, and which are active by day. In eastern and southern Australia the most commonly encountered members of this group are the Copper-tailed Skink (*Ctenotus taeniolatus*) and the Water Skink (*Sphenomorphus quoyii*). The Copper-tailed Skink (Plate 28) is a 6-inch, egg-laying lizard which feeds on insects and is generally found in rocky areas along the coast and ranges; a related species, *Ctenotus atlas*, is usually taken in clumps of porcupine grass from inland New South Wales to Western Australia.

The Water Skink, on the other hand, is a live-bearing species which is found among streamside rocks, logs, and vegetation. It is olive above with scattered black flecks, while the sides are black with white spotting; it will dive into the water if threatened, remaining there for some time until the danger has passed.

Somewhat resembling the Water Skink, but found throughout most parts of mainland Australia, is the Striped Skink (*Ctenotus robustus*), a species of the heathland or open forest. It is olive or brown in colour with alternate stripes of white and dark brown, and is fast and agile.

The other groups within the genus *Spheno-morphus* consist of nocturnal, burrowing lizards which tend to be banded rather than striped. The best-known is the Desert Banded Skink (*Sphenomorphus fasciolatus*). This lizard grows to about 6 inches in length and is found in dry, sandy country from central coastal Queensland through the interior of that State and New South Wales to Western Australia. It is insectivorous and is said to produce live young.

Possibly the sole Australian representative of a group of Asian lizards is the Rain-forest Skink (*Tropidophorus queenslandiae*), a rough-

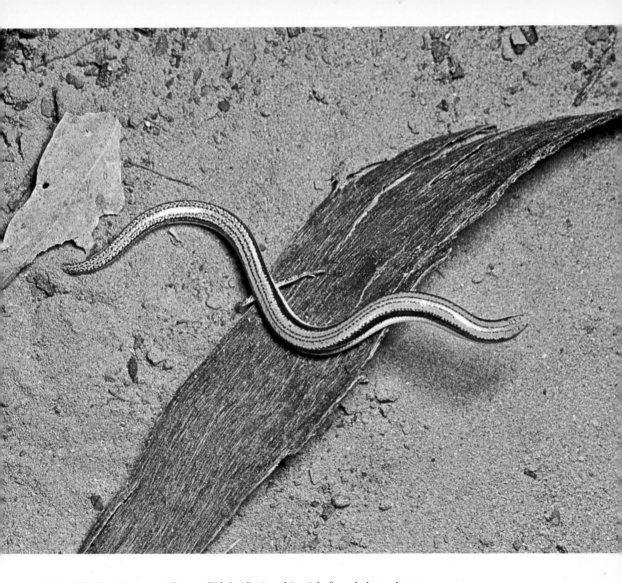

Plate 32. The Two-toed Desert Skink (*Lerista bipes*) is found throughout much of the arid interior of Australia. [Photo Author]

scaled, sombre-coloured lizard which is found only in the rain-forests of north Queensland. Growing to about 6 inches in length it is usually found during the day in a drowsy condition under rotting logs on the forest floor; virtually nothing is known of its habits or relationships.

As already mentioned, the reduction or loss of limbs has occurred independently in several groups of Australian skinks. The most extreme example is that of the Forest Worm Skink (*Anomalopus frontalis*), a foot-long, brown, burrowing skink from the rain forests of northern Queensland. It has a sharply-pointed snout and is without any sign of limbs, so is quite snake-like in appearance.

Rather more slender, but about the same length, is Verreaux's Skink (*Anomalopus verreauxii*), which ranges from south-eastern Queensland to the coast and ranges of northern New South Wales. It too is brown, but sometimes has a yellow or orange band across its nape. Its limbs are still present, but are reduced to tiny stumps which play little or no part in locomotion. The front pair of legs have three minute toes while the hind legs each have only a single toe.

In the drier parts of the continent are numerous species of burrowing, degenerate-limbed skinks belonging to the genus *Lerista*. Nearly all are pink or brown, sometimes with black stripes along their bodies, and between them they display varying degrees of limb degeneration. In all of them the limbs are small, but the number of toes on each foot varies from species to species.

All of these degenerate-limbed skinks are burrowers, and all appear to be strictly insectivorous. Some are egg-layers, while others produce live young. Some, like the Three-toed Skink (*Saiphos equalis*) of coastal Queensland and New South Wales illustrate an intermediate stage between the strictly egg-laying and the live-bearing forms. In this species the embryos are in an advanced stage within the soft-shelled eggs when the latter are laid, and usually hatch within a few days. In most egg-laying reptiles the eggs incubate for six weeks or more before hatching.

The classification of Australian skinks has undergone radical changes in recent years. As has already been mentioned in the Introduction, only those names which have been widely accepted have been used in this section.

Plate 33. A Forest Skink (*Egernia rugosa*) from Rockhampton in Queensland. [Photo Author]

BLIND SNAKES

Family *Typhlopidae*

FEW REPTILES are more maligned yet so poorly known as the blind or worm snakes. Indeed, so little is known about these reptiles that a study by two prominent American biologists has suggested that blind snakes are not really snakes but lizards!

More than 20 species have been recorded from continental Australia (none occur in Tasmania). They are found in all life zones, from the central-ian deserts to the rain-forests of Cape York Peninsula. A relatively uniform mode of life is reflected in a surprising uniformity of structure. Their worm-like bodies are well adapted to life underground: the snout is projecting, and is used to force a passage through soil or sand; the mouth is small, curved, and well below and behind the snout, rather like that of a shark. The vestigial eyes are small, darkly pigmented spots under the semi-transparent scales on the head and it has been suggested that they can distinguish only different light intensities, but not objects.

The body extends back from the head with a uniformity of colour and thickness which largely accounts for their worm-like appearance. Unlike most other land snakes, blind snakes lack the broad belly scales which normally play such an important part in locomotion. Instead, their small, smooth and highly polished scales are uniform around the body, allowing the snake to move through soil with a minimum of resistance. The tail, generally less than 1 inch long, terminates in a blunt spine which is pushed into the soil and helps to force the body through the earth.

This spine is popularly believed to be poisonous, and when handled it is pressed into one's flesh; it is both painless and harmless however.

Although colour varies from species to species, blind snakes are characteristically grey-brown to black above, and pinkish-white below. Variation between species is most marked in the shape of the head, which may be blunt or round, or sharply pointed, or made up of two or three distinct "lobes".

Blind snakes are non-venomous and harmless. The largest Australian species rarely attain a length of 2 feet, and most are considerably smaller.

Although blind snakes are often found under logs and stones, they are active above ground only at night or after heavy rain. They are known to feed on a variety of soil animals, including worms and the eggs and larvae of ants. Many species are found in termite mounds, and their distribution is almost undoubtedly closely correlated with that of the termites on which they feed. When first caught blind snakes often emit a foul-smelling secretion about which little is known. Although used as an offensive device, its primary function may be concerned with sex or trail recognition. Like other reptiles, blind snakes shed their skins at intervals, but these are rarely seen as they are shed below ground.

So far as is known, all blind snakes are egg-layers, but details of reproductive behaviour, and the number and form of the eggs, are virtually unknown for all Australian species. Unfortunately their subterranean habits have so far discouraged studies of their biology and ecology.

All Australian members of this family belong to the genus *Ramphotyphlops*.

Plate 34. *Ramphotyphlops nigrescens,* a common blind snake of eastern
Australia. [Photo Author]

PYTHONS

Family *Boidae*

THE PYTHONS (sub-family Pythoninae), together with the closely related boas (sub-family Boinae), contain most of the snakes which make up this non-venomous family. Whereas the boas are characteristic of the Americas, the pythons are Old World snakes, ranging from Africa through Asia and the Indo-Malayan Archipelago to Australia.

The largest of all Australian snakes, indeed one of the largest in the world, is the Amethystine or Rock Python of northern Queensland. Occasionally reaching a length in excess of 25 feet, the Amethystine Python (*Liasis amethystinus*) is nonetheless shy and inoffensive. It is one of some nine or 10 species of pythons that are found in Australia, and which range in size from the giant Amethystine Python (Plate 36) to the Pygmy Python (*Liasis perthensis*) a diminutive species by python standards, for it rarely attains a length of more than 2 feet.

All Australian pythons are able climbers, some of them spending much of their lives in trees or shrubs. Compared with other Australian snakes their scales are relatively small, which in turn allows their skin to stretch more, so that they can accommodate relatively larger items of food. Their belly scales, too, are not as broad as in most land snakes and are often ridged as an aid to climbing.

There are two small claws or spurs found in most pythons, situated one on either side of the vent, which represent the vestiges of hind limb structures. The spurs are generally much larger in males than females and have taken on a secondary sexual function, being used to stimulate the female prior to, and during mating.

In Australia, pythons are most plentiful in species and numbers in the northern parts of the continent. None are found in Tasmania. The best known and most widely distributed of all is the Carpet Snake (*Morelia spilotes variegata*) (Plate 35), a python growing to more than 10 feet in length. It is found throughout most parts of Australia except coastal New South Wales and much of Victoria. Although common in the drier inland parts of all States, it is only rarely encountered in the true desert country of Central and Western Australia. The Carpet Snake is very variable in colour and pattern, but is typically a shade of rich brown with blotches or cross-bands of darker brown edged with black. Brilliantly patterned forms, with contrasting bands and blotches of black edged with yellow and chocolate-brown are found in some of the wet, densely forested parts of north-eastern Queensland.

Like most Australian pythons, the Carpet Snake is largely nocturnal in its habits, though it sometimes likes to bask in the sun. In forest areas it is usually found at night, a few feet from the ground in low shrubs or trees, resting during the day in hollow logs, stumps, or hollow limbs of trees. In the drier inland regions it spends more time on the ground, and is often found in or around rabbit warrens, for rabbits are much sought after as food. Nevertheless it will often take to trees in search of birds and mammals.

A close relative of the Carpet Snake is the Diamond Snake (*Morelia spilotes spilotes*). In all except colour the Diamond Snake is similar to the Carpet Snake, although it does not grow quite as large, averaging only 6 feet in length and rarely exceeding 8 feet. The Diamond Snake is found only in the coastal forests of New South Wales. It is glossy greenish-black, many of

Plate 35. The Carpet Snake (*Morelia spilotes variegata*). [Photo S. Breeden]

its scales having cream or yellow spots; these spots may be scattered irregularly over the body or may be arranged in irregular blotches or diamond-shaped clumps. In occasional specimens the yellow colouring predominates over the black. In both the Carpet and Diamond Snakes the belly is yellowish with dark blotches. Both snakes are often used by farmers in barns and fodder stores in an effort to control rats and mice.

The Amethystine Python, already mentioned, is sometimes confused with the Carpet Snake, but may be readily distinguished by the regular pattern of enlarged shields on the head (these are broken up and irregular on the heads of Diamond and Carpet Snakes). In colour it is olive-brown with a banded or network pattern of darker brown. Underneath it is cream-coloured. Largely restricted to the rain-forests or wet sclerophyl forests of north-eastern Queensland, the Amethystine Python can often be found basking on the edges of clearings, from which it can quickly retreat into denser scrub. However, it is essentially a nocturnal hunter of birds and mammals. Despite the great length to which it can grow, it is not a particularly bulky snake. A 10 to 15-foot specimen would seldom have a girth thicker than a man's arm.

Two large pythons closely related to the Amethystine Python are the Brown Water Python (*Liasis fuscus*) and the Olive Rock Python (*Liasis olivaceus*). Both species grow to a length of more than 9 feet and are more or less uniform light to dark olive-brown with scales which are sleekly irridescent. The Brown Water Python is found throughout the northern parts of the continent, its range extending, via river systems, inland from the coast. Although it is usually met near streams or lagoons it may also be found considerable distances from water. The Olive Rock Python is generally restricted to the forested coastal parts of northern Australia.

Only in the dense rain-forests along the eastern parts of Cape York Peninsula have occasional specimens of the Green Tree Python (*Chondropython viridis*) been found. This beautiful python is common in New Guinea and is evidently a fairly recent migrant to Australia. Adults are bright emerald green, with yellowish-white markings along the centre of the back. In contrast to the brilliant green of the adults the young are typically bright lemon-yellow to orange. The Green Tree Python, as its name implies, spends most of its life in trees and shrubs, where it feeds largely on birds and mammals.

There are two Australian pythons which are not at all python-like in their appearance. Whereas most pythons have broad, conspicuous heads, these two have narrow, somewhat pointed heads, and are often mistaken for venomous elapid snakes. They are the Woma (*Aspidites ramsayi*), and the Black-headed Python (*Aspidites melanocephalus*) (Plate 37), snakes that are so closely related that some herpetologists consider they are only geographic races of the same species. Both are nocturnal, ground-living snakes, and are similar in their habits.

The Woma inhabits the arid centre of Australia, extending outwards into the dry inland of all mainland States except Victoria. It is grey-brown with numerous dark brown bands along the

Plate 36. The Amethystine Python (*Liasis amethystinus*), Australia's largest snake. [Photo Author]

length of its body, and is whitish below. The Black-headed Python is similarly banded, but its head and nape are shiny black and the body is rich brown with dark chocolate-brown bands. It is found throughout a broad area of northern Australia.

Pythons are non-venomous "constricting" snakes; that is, they kill their prey by throwing tight coils of their bodies around it until it suffocates. Contrary to popular belief, they do not physically crush their prey, and its tissues remain intact. They feed almost exclusively on backboned animals, more especially on the warm-blooded birds and mammals; only when newborn do they sometimes feed on insects. The Black-headed Python is a notorious snake-eater, and rarely comes off second-best even in encounters with venomous species.

Pythons are able to eat animals which at first sight appear much too large to be swallowed. Like all other snakes, they do not chew their food, but swallow it whole; their jaws, like those of other snakes, are so loosely articulated, and their skin so distendable, that they can swallow an object many times their own girth. Once caught in their jaws an animal has little chance of escaping from the numerous, strong, back-wardly curved teeth.

Australian pythons are egg-layers, and unlike most other snakes the female both protects and incubates the eggs until they hatch. During this time she coils around the eggs, which are piled into a clump; she may leave the eggs briefly to warm herself by basking in the sun, after which she returns to her position and transfers some heat to the eggs. In zoos, some incubating pythons have been found to produce heat internally by a little-understood mechanism involving rapid muscle spasms; this physiological heat production can raise the snake's temperature by several degrees Celsius above that of its surroundings. Whether this method is normally used by pythons in the wild to elevate their body temperatures during incubation is not yet known.

Plate 37. The Black-headed Python (*Aspidites melanocephalus*). [Photo Author]

COLUBRID SNAKES

Family *Colubridae*

THIS, the largest and most widely-ranging group of snakes in the world, has fewer species in Australia than any other family with representatives in this country. It contains such a conglomeration of species whose relationships to each other are anything but clear, that the classification within the family has had a history of almost constant change. If this is confusing to the herpetologist it surely baffles and misleads the layman.

The origins of the members of this family are obscure, but it is now generally agreed that most of them have evolved from a common ancestral form. It is for this reason that despite vast differences between the various members living today, they are all placed together in a single family. Nevertheless natural groups of related species are placed within distinct sub-families, most of which have representatives in Australia.

Colubrid snakes may be egg-layers or live-bearers; generally the former tend to be land-living forms while the latter tend to be aquatic. The family contains both venomous and non-venomous snakes, the venomous species being called "rear-fanged" because, unlike the venomous snakes described in the next section, their fangs are at the rear of the mouth. The fangs are rather less efficient than those of other venomous snakes, being little more than slightly enlarged teeth, each with a groove running down its surface. The duct from the venom gland opens at the base of the groove, venom being expelled by muscular contractions around the gland.

Although colubrid snakes have proved to be one of the most successful groups in the world, their poor representation in Australia is probably no more than a reflection of their relatively recent arrival in this country. The land-dwelling species appear to have arrived in one or more waves of migration that probably took place when enlarged polar ice-caps during the Great Ice Ages of the Pleistocene period lowered the sea level and made a land bridge between Australia and New Guinea. (See Introduction.) Several of the water snakes probably arrived on the north coast simply by swimming there from the islands to the north.

The largest group within this family is the sub-family Colubrinae, whose members are non-venomous. The most common Australian species is the Green Tree Snake (*Dendrelaphis punctulatus*) (Plate 38), which is found on the coast and ranges and along some of the inland rivers of New South Wales, through Queensland and across the north of the continent to the Kimberley district in Western Australia. It is variable in colour, but is usually grey, brown or olive-green above and greenish-yellow on the belly. The throat is often a beautiful lemon-yellow. In various northern parts of Australia, black, and sometimes blue specimens are found. Whether any of the many colour forms known represent distinct species has yet to be determined.

As the name implies, the Green Tree Snake spends much of its life off the ground in shrubs or trees. It is a snake which often forms small colonies in rock outcrops, or even in houses in suburban areas. It is very slender and agile, appearing to move at incredible speed through thick foliage, and will often descend rapidly from a tree by literally dropping from one branch to another below. The belly scales have special ridges which assist the snake in climbing. It is, incidentally, a sun-loving snake which is active by day, feeding on frogs and nestling birds.

The Green Tree Snake grows to about 6 feet.

Plate 38. A Green Tree Snake (*Dendrelaphis punctulatus*) from the Cobourg Peninsula in the Northern Territory. [Photo Author]

When annoyed it inflates its body with air, so that the bright blue skin between the scales is clearly visible. This is especially marked in the region of the neck, which is flattened vertically to make that part of the body appear larger than normal. Holding the head and the neck off the ground in a long low curve, the snake will bite savagely and repeatedly if provoked.

Another member of this non-venomous family is the Fresh-water Snake (*Amphiesma mairii*) (Plate 39). This is a ground-dwelling snake that is usually found in or near swamps or streams, where it feeds largely on frogs. It varies from grey to rich brown in colour, its ridged scales giving it a rough appearance. It is found along the coastal areas of northern and eastern Australia to northern New South Wales.

Another common member of this sub-family is the Slatey-grey Snake (*Stegonotus cucullatus*), a shiny, slate-grey to black 3-foot snake, common throughout the coastal parts of northern Australia. It is an able climber and, as it is active at night, is commonly encountered in outhouses and sheds, or around water tanks, where it feeds mainly on frogs. It strikes savagely and bites freely if molested and, like other Australian members of this group, is an egg-laying species.

Another non-venomous sub-family, although sometimes regarded as a distinct family, is the Acrochordinae, or file snakes. The two members of this group are common along the coast and streams of northern Australia. The largest and best-known is the Javan File Snake (*Acrochordus javanicus*), a flabby, brown, 6-foot-plus, fish-eating snake, which rarely, if ever, leaves the water. The Javan File Snake is largely nocturnal in its habits, resting during the day in crevices and under ledges along the banks of streams and lagoons.

File snakes are so named because each of their scales has a blunt ridge which makes the skin rough and file-like to touch. Both species are widely distributed throughout Asia and the Indo-Malayan Archipelago to Australia, and produce live young.

The remaining two Australian sub-families are venomous, rear-fanged snakes.

The sub-family Boiginae includes one Australian species of Brown Tree Snake (*Boiga irregularis*) (Plate 40), in which, like the Green Tree Snake, occasional exceptionally bright-coloured forms are found in parts of northern Australia. Its distribution, too, parallels that of the Green Tree Snake, for it ranges from the coastal and near-coastal areas of central New South Wales through Queensland across the top of the Northern Territory to the Kimberleys. It is a nocturnal snake, brown above, with irregular dark cross-bands and a salmon-coloured belly. Its head is very broad and distinct from the neck, while its eyes are relatively large; in some places it goes by such names as the Dolls'-eye Snake and the Night Tiger. It is a tree-living snake which feeds largely on birds and small mammals, against which its venom seems to be quite potent. No serious effects on humans have ever been reported, but as some specimens reach a length of more than 7 feet such giants should be treated with caution.

As a result of its partiality for birds and their eggs the Brown Tree Snake often finds itself in a predicament similar to that of Pooh Bear after his visit to Rabbit; although small enough when hungry to slide through the wire of a birdcage or aviary, once having fed, the snake's girth has so increased that it can't escape! This species bites savagely when annoyed; throwing the front part of its body into a series of curves it can raise itself high off the ground or hang from a branch, striking successfully from a distance that seems deceptively safe.

Plate 39. The Fresh-water Snake (*Amphiesma mairii*). [Photo S. Breeden]

The only other sub-family with representatives in Australia is the Homalopsinae, a group of rear-fanged water snakes with four or five members found around the tropical north Australian coast. Although fairly common, they are not often seen and little is known of their general habits. All appear to be live-bearing, although the number of young produced is not known. Little is known, too, of their venom but none appears to be harmful to man. They are generally found in mangrove swamps, on mud flats, or around the banks of fresh water and tidal rivers; although they like to bask, they are generally most active at night, when they forage for fish, crabs, and other aquatic animals. Like the true sea-snakes, all have valvular nostrils on top of the head which allow them to seal their respiratory passages when they submerge.

The Bockadam (*Cerberus australis*) is one of the prettiest members of this group. Grey above, with irregular dark spots and cross-bands, its sides are sometimes richly flushed with pink or salmon, while underneath it is yellow or white with black bands. It grows to a length of about 2 feet and has a broad, rather ugly head.

Most colubrids, having no venom with which to subdue their prey, constrict it in rather the same way as do the pythons. Even the venomous rear-fanged colubrids tend to use this method. On many occasions, however, the prey is actually swallowed alive to be killed by suffocation and the action of the digestive juices.

Plate 40. A Brown Tree Snake (*Boiga irregularis*) from Cape York Peninsula. [Photo Author]

ELAPID SNAKES

Family *Elapidae*

OF ABOUT 110 different kinds of land snakes found in Australia, roughly 60 per cent belong to this family of venomous snakes. This ratio of venomous to non-venomous land snakes gives Australia the somewhat dubious distinction of having the highest proportion of venomous land snakes of any country in the world. This is not quite as frightening as it might first appear, for only a small number of Australian elapid snakes are dangerous to man; the majority of species are relatively small, with biting mechanisms and venoms which are effective against only the small animals on which they feed.

Despite their diversity in Australia, no common name has ever been coined for the family in this country and the adjective "elapid" is simply derived from the scientific name. Elapid snakes are found in all the continents of the world and they include such well-known and dangerous snakes as the African and Asian cobras, the African mambas, the Asian kraits, and the coral snakes of the Americas. Against this formidable line-up the Australian elapids can hold their own, for the venoms of such species as the Tiger Snake (*Notechis scutatus*) (Plate 41) and the Taipan (*Oxyuranus scutellatus*) are more potent than those of any of their foreign relatives. This alarming statement needs to be qualified, however, for despite the potency of their venoms Australia's dangerous snakes are responsible for an average of only about four deaths every year.

The chief characteristic of elapid snakes is a pair of hollow fangs at the front of the upper jaws, the base of each fang being connected by a duct to a gland which produces venom, the gland on each side lying just below and behind the eye.

The venom-carrying hollow in each fang is formed by the closure of a deep groove down the front surface of the fang. The fangs are immovably fixed to the jaws and, like the other teeth, are replaced by new ones at regular intervals; at any one time there may be several pairs of fangs lying in position, one pair functional, and one or more pairs of replacement fangs. When a snake bites, muscles contract the venom glands to force venom down each duct and through the hollow fangs.

The diet of most elapid snakes is fairly catholic, the size of a particular snake being the main factor determining its feeding habits. Of course species living in swampy areas are likely to have a preference for frogs, whereas desert snakes might subsist almost entirely on lizards and small mammals. However, apart from the lack of choice dictated by a particular environment, most large elapid snakes will feed on frogs, other reptiles, small mammals, and even on birds when these are accessible. Smaller specimens, whether the young of larger species or adults of smaller forms, are usually found to subsist on small frogs or lizards, or even insects. The latter are especially prominent in the diet of burrowing snakes. Some species, like the Mulga Snake, are noted cannibals which frequently feed on other snakes. Many snake parents will eat their own young if given the opportunity.

Not a great deal is known about reproduction in elapid snakes; in the case of many of the smaller and rarer species it is not even known whether they lay eggs or bear their young alive. In the southern parts of Australia, the breeding season usually extends from about mid-October to the end of December. At least some specimens, though it is not known what proportion of the population, produce two batches of eggs or young, usually two months or more apart, and

Plate 41. The Tiger Snake (*Notechis scutatus*) is found throughout many parts of southern Australia. [Photo Author]

typically in January and March. This difference in time between the breeding or mating season and the hatching or laying season reflects the average time it takes for eggs to hatch after being laid, or the length of the gestation period in live-bearing species – about eight weeks. Most young are born in February or early March. These figures are only average, for up to the present time no species of elapid snake has ever been studied intensely enough to provide an accurate picture of its biology and life history.

As one moves into northern Australia the picture changes, for there most species appear to lack a definite breeding season. It is not known, however, whether species in this part of Australia produce more than one brood each year.

Little is known, too, of any mating displays or behaviour patterns in Australian elapids, except for the twisting and coiling manoeuvres of the male when attempting to put himself in a favourable position for mating with the female. Typically the male approaches the female from behind, and sliding along her body he throws several loops of his body around or over hers until their vents are opposite. The male sometimes bites and grips the female at some point along her neck, presumably to assist him in getting a purchase on her body. The male has two separate organs of reproduction which, though they are termed "hemipenes", function independently of one another. They normally lie in special sacs within the base of the tail, and are extruded only during mating. Each is covered by a series of spines and furrows, their arrangement often varying from species to species. Only one penis is used during mating.

The males of a number of species have been observed fighting during the breeding season. In the Eastern Brown Snake (*Pseudonaja textilis*) and the Red-bellied Black Snake (*Pseudechis*

porphyriacus) (Plate 45) fighting males intertwine their bodies and bite each other savagely about the head and neck, each striving for an advantageous position over the other. The purpose of these fights is little understood, and the outcome is seldom observed, though David Fleay reports that the females watch these encounters. Incidentally it has been shown quite clearly that most Australian snakes are more or less immune to their own venom, though it is not known whether this immunity is inherited or developed during the snake's lifetime. Its advantages are obvious, for in fighting or mating, in capturing its prey, or in defending itself from its enemies, a snake may easily be bitten, either by itself (accidentally) or by another snake.

Among the larger, dangerous elapids only the Taipan and the various Brown Snakes lay eggs. The others are live-bearing, the young actually hatching from unshelled eggs within the body of the mother, so that they are born as live and active youngsters which are replicas of their parents. Only in a few species are the young very different in appearance from the adults, and then only in colour and pattern. Probably the best-known example is that of the Common or Eastern Brown Snake. In many parts of eastern Australia the young Brown Snakes, when they hatch from the eggs, have a black head, a broad black band on the nape and a series of narrow black bands along the length of their bodies. As they grow the body bands soon disappear, leaving only the markings on the head and nape. Eventually even these disappear to leave the typically uniform brown adult.

Elapid snakes, like all other kinds, shed their skins from time to time. Young specimens, whose growth is proportionately much greater than that of adults, shed their skin more frequently. Shedding their skin is often the very first action

Plate 42. The Death Adder (*Acanthophis antarcticus*) is found throughout most parts of Australia. [Photo Author]

of new-born snakes, and may take place within minutes of their birth. The skin is usually shed whole, and the process begins when the skin around the lips is pulled back. By rubbing the body against any rough surface the skin is pushed back gradually over the body so that when shedding is completed the skin is actually inside out.

The Australian bush has an undeserved reputation, abroad as well as at home, of being "alive" with snakes. One wonders how such a reputation arose, for in most parts of Australia it is rarely easy to find, let alone be found by, a snake, either harmless or venomous. Concentrations of snakes do sometimes occur, but these are exceptional. They are usually seasonal and may occur naturally as a result of periodic inundation of the flood plains of inland rivers and lakes. Along the Murray River, for example, concentrations of Tiger Snakes are often found; while at Lake Narran, in northern New South Wales, Brown Snakes are sometimes so common that a person standing on the black soil near the lake's edge might see four or five snakes in a single sweeping glance. Such concentrations of snakes may also occur under man-made conditions in large irrigation areas. On some islands, when food is plentiful and predators are few, snakes are often able to build up their numbers to greater concentrations than occur in mainland populations of the same species.

Despite their colourful reputations to the contrary, virtually all Australian snakes are shy and retiring and the venomous elapids are no exception. The Tiger Snake has probably the most evil reputation for aggressiveness of any Australian snake, yet given the opportunity it will almost invariably flee at the approach of a human. This is equally true of the Taipan, which also has an undeserved reputation for innate aggressiveness. This is not to say that these, and others, will not defend themselves savagely if cornered or attacked, for they certainly will. But this behaviour, together with that so often shown by caged specimens in zoos, is very different from that normally encountered in the wild.

Australian elapid snakes range from small burrowing species, hardly more than a foot in length, to the large and deadly Taipan, which attains a length of more than 10 feet. They are found in every life zone in Australia, from the tropical rain-forests of the north-east to the deserts of the interior. Of the three snakes found in Tasmania, all are members of this family. It is impossible to mention more than a few common species in a book of this size.

Most elapid snakes are terrestrial; they may be found under rocks or in rock crevices, in or under logs and other fallen timber, or in burrows made by other animals. With the possible exception of the Broad-headed Snakes of eastern Australia, especially the Pale-headed Snake (*Hoplocephalus bitorquatus*), elapid snakes are never arboreal, even in areas where arboreal snakes of other families are absent.

The richest variety of species is found in the relatively wet coastal and near-coastal parts of eastern and north-eastern Australia. None are restricted to the tropical and sub-tropical rain-forests and most of the species found there are simply representatives of more widely ranging forms. They are usually found beside streams or paths and are rarely encountered in the depths of the forest. Two such species are the Red-bellied Black Snake (*Pseudechis porphyriacus*) (Plate 45) and the Black-bellied Swamp Snake (*Hemiaspis signata*). The latter grows to nearly 3 feet in length, is dark brown above and black or dark grey below, and is found in coastal regions from

Plate 43. A Copperhead (*Austrelaps superba*) from the northern tablelands of New South Wales. [Photo Author]

northern Queensland to southern New South Wales.

Two other small snakes commonly encountered along the eastern coast are the White-crowned Snake (*Cacophis harriettae*) and the Golden-crowned Snake (*Cacophis squamulosus*) both of which rarely grow to more than 2 feet in length. The White-crowned Snake is dark brown with a dark grey belly and broad white band across the nape; it is found most commonly in south-eastern Queensland. The Golden-crowned Snake is most common on the north coast of New South Wales, but is frequently found even in the inner suburbs of Sydney; it, too, is dark brown above, but is pink or red on the belly and has a yellowish band around the side and front of the head which doesn't quite meet on the nape.

In the inland of New South Wales, Queensland and South Australia one of the most common elapid snakes is the Myall Snake (*Suta suta*), a species with rich brown body, black or dark brown head and nape, and white belly. The Myall Snake (Plate 48) inflates and flattens its body when annoyed, throwing it into a spring-like coil rather like that of a Death Adder. Its bite can be extremely painful.

Somewhat similar to the Myall Snake in colour pattern, but smaller in size, are the Black-headed Snake (*Unechis gouldii*) and the Little Whip Snake (*Unechis flagellum*.) Both are rich brown above with shiny black head and nape, and white below; they seldom reach a length of 2 feet. The Black-headed Snake is found from inland Queensland through New South Wales and South Australia to Western Australia; except for a small area between Sydney and the Hunter River Valley it does not occur on the coast of New South Wales. The Little Whip Snake is common on the outskirts of Melbourne and extends into the southern parts of New South

Wales and westward into South Australia.

In the open forests of south-western Australia one of the most common of the smaller elapids is the Western Bandy Bandy (*Simoselaps bertholdi*), which rarely reaches more than 15 inches in length. It varies from cream to yellowish or even reddish with numerous black cross-bands.

Some elapid snakes are found virtually through-out the continent, from the wetter coastal regions to the arid interior. One of these is the Yellow-faced Whip Snake (*Demansia psammophis*) (Plate 46), an olive-grey-brown snake with a comma-shaped yellow ring around each eye. Growing to more than 3 feet in length, it is found in all States except Tasmania. With an almost equally broad distribution is the Common Bandy Bandy (*Vermicella annulata*) (Plate 47), a burrow-ing snake with alternate black and white rings along the length of its body.

Most of the elapid snakes found in Australia's desert regions are merely representatives of more widely-distributed forms, and little is known of the ways in which they are adapted to life in such a harsh environment. Whether these snakes have evolved any of the complex physiological adaptations found in other reptiles is not known, as most, if not all, are nocturnal; it seems possible that they are able to survive there not so much by adapting to the true desert conditions but largely by living in places such as burrows and rock crevices, where they can avoid climatic extremes.

As this family contains the only dangerous snakes to be encountered in the Australian bush, interest in them not unnaturally centres on those species known to be potential killers, and to complete this chapter these snakes will be treated in somewhat greater detail.

Seldom are more than three or four species of

Plate 44. One of the many colour forms of the Western Brown Snake (*Pseudonaja nuchalis*). [Photo Author]

dangerous snakes found in any given area in Australia, so that it should not be too difficult for most people to learn to recognise the dangerous species of their district. As a guide, Australia's major dangerous snakes and their distribution are described briefly below. There are other species whose bites, in certain circumstances, might prove dangerous to children or even adults. However the snakes listed are the only ones known to have inflicted a fatal bite.

The TAIPAN (*Oxyuranus scutellatus*) is found throughout most of Queensland except the extreme south-eastern corner. It is also found in Arnhem Land and possibly in north-western Australia. Although it may grow to more than 10 feet in length, it averages only 5 to 6 feet. It is light to dark brown above and yellowish with orange flecks on the belly.

The FIERCE SNAKE (*Parademansia microlepidota*) is a large, highly-venomous snake found only in the drier parts of the region centred on the Queensland-South Australia border. Superficially similar to a Taipan, specimens reach a length of more than 6 feet.

The DEATH ADDER (*Acanthophis antarcticus*) (Plate 42) is found throughout most parts of Australia except Tasmania and the south-eastern corner of the continent. It has a broad head distinct from its neck, a thick body and a thin, rat-like tail which ends in a light-coloured, curved spine. The colour is usually grey or reddish-brown with irregular dark cross-bands. It averages less than 2 feet in length, the maximum size recorded being a little over 3 feet. The desert form, *pyrrhus*, is sometimes regarded as a distinct species.

The TIGER SNAKES (*Notechis scutatus*) (Plate 41) and *Notechis ater* are found in southern Australia, including Tasmania, from a little north of the Queensland border in the east to about Onslow in Western Australia. They vary greatly in colour, though mainland specimens are typically dull brown or olive above, with or without irregular dark cross-bands, and cream or yellow on the belly. Many island populations, as well as some on the mainland, are very dark brown to black above, occasionally with lighter cross-bands, and grey below. Mainland Tiger Snakes average only 3 to 4 feet in length, but the black forms on some Bass Strait islands are much larger, averaging 5 to 6 feet.

The EASTERN BROWN SNAKE (*Pseudonaja textilis*) is found throughout the length of eastern Australia, from Cape York to Victoria and extending into the southern parts of South Australia. In central inland New South Wales the western limits of its range overlap with the eastern limits of the Western Brown Snake. The Eastern Brown Snake grows to more than 7 feet. It is light to dark brown above and cream, with orange blotches, on the belly. The newly-hatched young are black-headed and are sometimes banded. It is a slender, agile snake typically found under dry conditions.

The WESTERN BROWN SNAKE (*Pseudonaja nuchalis*) (Plate 44) is found from inland New South Wales and Queensland through the centre of the continent to Western Australia where a northern form is known as the Gwardar and a southern form, sometimes regarded as a distinct species, as the Dugite. The Western Brown Snake is similar in shape, size, and habits to the Eastern Brown Snake, but is much more variable in colour. It varies from olive-grey to rich brown above, often with dark-edged scales which form irregular narrow cross-bands. The head is often black, and there may be a series of black scales on the nape. The belly may be salmon-coloured to cream, usually with scattered orange blotches.

98

Plate 45. The Red-bellied Black Snake (*Pseudechis porphyriacus*), one of the most common snakes in eastern Australia, is usually found near water. [Photo Author]

The COPPERHEAD (*Austrelaps superbus*) (Plate 43) is found only in the south-eastern corner of Australia, including Tasmania. In New South Wales it is found only in the colder mountainous areas and highlands, while in South Australia it is found only as far west as the Mt Lofty Ranges and Kangaroo Island. The Copperhead averages only 3 to 4 feet in length. It is typically dark brown to almost black above, though light brown individuals are sometimes found. Young specimens often have a conspicuous yellow band across the nape. Most Copperheads have distinctively barred lips, as shown in Plate 43, but some Victorian populations lack these markings.

The MULGA SNAKE (*Pseudechis australis*) is found throughout northern Australia and in the drier, inland parts of the southern half of Australia. It grows to more than 8 feet in length, and is typically a uniform light to rich reddish-brown above and salmon-coloured below.

The RED-BELLIED BLACK SNAKE (*Pseudechis porphyriacus*) (Plate 45) is closely related to the Mulga Snake, but is very different in colour. It has a shiny black head and body and is typically pink to bright red on the belly. It is found in eastern Australia from Cape York to South Australia. Although it averages only about 5 feet, it may grow to more than 7 feet.

The SPOTTED BLACK SNAKE (*Pseudechis guttatus*) is similar in size and build to its close relative the Red-bellied Black Snake. It may be uniformly black above, or black with scattered light spots. The belly is blue-grey. This species is found west of the Great Dividing Range in southern Queensland and the northern half of New South Wales, though it reaches the coast through the Hunter River Valley.

The only other known killer is the ROUGH-SCALED SNAKE (*Tropidechis carinatus*). It is found along the eastern coast from Barrington Tops in New South Wales to the Cairns district of northern Queensland. It resembles a typical banded mainland Tiger Snake, but can be readily distinguished by its strongly-ridged scales. It rarely grows to more than 4 feet in length.

Which of all these is Australia's deadliest snake? This apparently simple question is, in reality, very complex and difficult to answer, for there are different ways in which the deadliness of a snake can be measured. The effects of a snake bite depend on many variable factors, including the size of the person bitten, his state of health, the position of the bite, the size and health of the snake, the time elapsed since it last fed, and the effectiveness of the treatment. Probably the most realistic comparison is between the potential killing power of the *average* amount of venom injected by various species of snakes when they bite. If this is done then the relative "deadliness" of Australian snakes is in roughly the same order as the snakes discussed above.

Snake venom is essentially a complex mixture of proteins, the components and their proportions varying greatly from species to species or from family to family. Not all components of snake venom have been fully studied and their actions understood, but the major components have been placed into broad categories largely according to their effects.

Of these basic components:

Haemorrhagins destroy the linings of blood-vessels, allowing blood to escape into the surrounding tissues.

Haemolysins destroy the red blood corpuscles.

Neurotoxins act on the nervous system, usually causing death by asphyxiation when the nerves

Plate 46. The Yellow-faced Whip Snake (*Demansia psammophis*) is found in most parts of Australia. This brightly-coloured specimen is from Coober Pedy in South Australia. [Photo Author]

controlling the heart and lungs are put out of action.

Thrombase causes clotting of the blood within the blood-vessels.

Cytolysins destroy red and white blood corpuscles and tissue cells.

Anticoagulins retard clotting of the blood.

There are several other components which, though important, do not generally play a significant role in the dangerous effects of snake-bite. They include various ferments which are important in preparing a snake's food for digestion.

Not all of these components are necessarily present in the venom of a particular species. Elapid snake venoms are characterised by being especially rich in neurotoxins, so that their major effect is on the nervous system. Neurotoxic venoms are usually those most feared throughout the world because, as they act directly on the vital control centres of the body, their effects appear rapidly and make treatment difficult. Those venoms which act principally on the blood can cause horrifying local effects, but their action on the vital centres is less rapid and therefore allows more time for effective treatment.

Even among closely related snakes, a component present in one species may be absent in another. Thrombase is an important constituent of the venoms of the Taipan, Tiger Snake, Brown Snakes, and Black Snakes, but is absent in those of the Death Adder and Copperhead. The Red-bellied Black Snake and the Copperhead have venoms much richer in both cytolysins and haemolysins than other Australian species.

The most modern and effective treatment of snake-bite involves the use of snake-bite sera or antivenenes. Basically these are prepared by the injection into a horse of a series of gradually increasing doses of venom over a period of time, the initial doses being too small to do the horse any harm. In this way the horse builds up an immunity to the venom by producing antibodies in its blood which destroy the venom. The serum from such a horse is refined to produce an antivenene.

The first antivenene in Australia was developed in 1929 for use against the Tiger Snake, but it was also used with partial success against the bites of other Australian snakes. This success was due to the fact, as already explained, that although the venoms of the different species of elapid snakes differ considerably from one another, they do have certain constituents in common.

In 1954 a specific antivenene against the bite of the Taipan was developed, and this was followed by a Death Adder antivenene in 1958 and a Brown Snake antivenene in 1961. The Commonwealth Serum Laboratories are now producing regional polyvalent antivenenes which contain a mixture of globulins antitoxic to the venoms of all the dangerous snakes in a particular region. Such polyvalent antivenenes are especially valuable because only rarely does a bitten person know the kind of snake responsible for the bite, making effective treatment very difficult.

Unfortunately many people suffer a reaction, of varying severity, to the horse serum which is the basis of the antivenene. With such people the antivenene can even prove fatal, and a patient is normally tested for allergy to the serum before being given a normal dose. If this is not done the antivenene might well prove to be more dangerous than the original snake-bite, especially when the snake responsible for the bite is a harmless one, as has often proved to be the case!

Plate 47. The Common Bandy Bandy (*Vermicella annulata*) grows to about 3 feet in length. It is not dangerous to man. [Photo Author]

SEA-SNAKES

Families *Hydrophiidae* and *Laticaudidae*

FOUND THROUGHOUT the tropical and subtropical waters of the Indo-Pacific region, sea-snakes are highly specialised reptiles whose adaptations to life in the sea are reflected in nearly every one of their visible characteristics. Most species live in the area between India and the north coast of Australia, only one species reaching as far as the Pacific coasts of America and Africa. All of them are venomous and nearly all of the venoms that have been tested have been found, on a drop-for-drop basis, to be extremely potent. Fortunately for humans, however, most sea-snakes have relatively short fangs and their biting mechanism is not as efficient as that of many larger-fanged dangerous land snakes, whose venoms are often not nearly as potent.

No deaths from sea-snake bites have been authoritatively recorded from Australia and bites are extremely rare. This is in sharp contrast to the numerous bites and frequent deaths recorded among native fishermen in Indonesia and Malaysia. Certainly, all our species should be treated as possible killers.

An important factor in limiting the number of sea-snake bites is the temperament of the snakes themselves. Almost without exception an unmolested sea-snake will not attempt to bite.

Unfortunately, however, the snakes are sometimes very curious, and their interest often shows itself as a rush towards the diver, which he, not unnaturally, interprets as an attack. The snakes may coil themselves around a diver's arms or legs and it is under these circumstances that he runs the risk of being bitten by unwittingly provoking the snake.

There seems to be little doubt that sea-snakes arose fairly late in reptilian evolution and that they are derived from a group of venomous land snakes closely related to the elapid snakes (Chapter 11). This relationship is reflected in many features, including the venom, which in these two groups of snakes is remarkably similar in its actions. Current research has thrown doubt on the traditional view of this family and its relationships. Some researchers recognise two distinct families, while others regard them simply as members of the family of elapid snakes. The high potency of sea-snake venom has probably evolved from the need to kill, quickly and efficiently, such active prey as fish.

Like other reptiles, sea-snakes breathe atmospheric oxygen and must therefore return to the surface periodically to replenish their air supply. Their lungs and air passages are especially modified to allow them to stay submerged for lengthy periods, though for just how long no one knows. Unlike typical land snakes, in which the nostrils are on the side of the head, the nostrils in sea-snakes are on top of the head and are

Plate 48. The Myall Snake (*Suta suta*), a common snake throughout the drier parts of southern Australia [Photo Author]

equipped with small flaps of skin which act as valves. Once a breath of air is taken at the surface, the valves close and the snake can submerge without water entering the air passages.

The most distinctive feature of a sea-snake is its flattened, paddle-shaped tail and it is this paddle which is the snake's main source of propulsion in the water. In most sea-snakes the body also is somewhat flattened and this assists in the sideways, eel-like undulations that are its normal movement. In land snakes the broad belly scales are used for crawling across rough surfaces; as few sea-snakes ever come onto land the belly scales have degenerated in most species until they are not a great deal larger than the rest of the body scales. Several sea-snakes are exceptional, however, in that they spend much of their lives on land. Of these, probably the best known is the common Banded Sea-snake (*Laticauda colubrina*) (Plate 50), which spends much of its time in mangrove swamps, on coral islands, or under ledges and crevices in bushy country some distance from the sea. Although *Laticauda* and its allies have typical paddle-shaped tails, their belly scales are broad like those of land snakes and are used in the same way. The Banded Sea-snake has its body ringed with numerous alternate bands of white or cream and blue-black.

In keeping with its terrestrial habits this species has unusual breeding habits for a sea-snake, for it lays up to about a dozen eggs on land. The true sea-snake produces live young which are born in the sea; the number does not appear to be as great as in land snakes of similar size, for only rarely are more than about 10 young produced at one time. These can fend for themselves as soon as they are born.

There are about 30-odd kinds of sea-snakes recorded from the tropical waters of Australia but most are rather nondescript and difficult to identify. Typically they range in colour from dull grey to brown, with or without darker bands. Many have brightly banded young but adults without bands, making colour and pattern of little use in identification.

Although sea-snakes are often found far out to sea, they are more plentiful in coastal or estuarine waters. There have been many reports from different parts of the Indo-Pacific of enormous concentrations of sea-snakes in a small area. Whether these concentrations are connected with migration or breeding is not known, though the latter seems to be more likely. One area in Australia where such concentrations have been frequently recorded is in the Swain Reefs, an immense complex of coral reefs and cays at the southern end of the Great Barrier Reef.

Simply because they live in the sea most sea-snakes are difficult to observe or collect, and for this reason they are one of the most poorly

Plate 49. The Elegant Banded Sea-snake (*Hydrophis elegans*) is found throughout the coastal waters of tropical Australia. [Photo S. Breeden]

known groups of reptiles in the world. It is not known whether they have a definite breeding season in Australian waters although females of one species, the Yellow-bellied Sea-snake (*Pelamis platurus*), have been found in the coastal waters of south-eastern Australia with well-formed young in their oviducts during the mid-winter months of June and July. The Yellow-bellied Sea-snake has a very distinctive colour pattern; the top half of its body is black, while the lower half ranges from bright yellow to dull brown. The two colours meet in a straight line in the middle of the body, without any mixing of the two. It is the most wide ranging of all the sea-snakes, being found from Africa across the Indian and Pacific Oceans to the west coast of the Americas. It is the most common species encountered on the coast of New South Wales, and all year round, after storms at sea, exhausted snakes are washed up on our beaches.

Few sea-snakes average more than 4 or 5 feet in length, although one or two kinds grow to between 7 and 9 feet. Most appear to be general fish-eaters, although some have been known to feed only on eels.

Plate 50. The Banded Sea-snake (*Laticauda colubrina*), though common throughout the tropical Pacific, is only occasionally found in southern Australian waters. [Photo Author]

INDEX

Bold figures indicate colour plates